MISSION: IMPOSSIBLE

ANNUAL 1972

CONTENTS

Published in Great Britain by
World Distributors (Manchester) Limited
P.O. Box 111, 12 Lever Street, Manchester M60 1TS

Printed in Italy

SBN 7235 0115 7

bang on target

"The underwater pod is located two miles east of a place called Katimura. It's fed by a supply line that connects with a cruiser. Security is very tight. . . ."

"And we're gonna find a way to get into it, I suppose," murmured Rollin.

The tape-recorder confirmed his guess as it spun the message from its anonymous little spool.

"The man you've got to get to is Doctor Grapler. He's a top scientist. He's being forced to work against his will on a new underwater warfare weapon. Apparently they are holding his family as hostages.

"Your prime mission is to get the new weapon. If you can also rescue Grapler and his family – so much the better. It will mean infiltrating the area, and trying to find out where the family is being held. For political reasons, we can offer you no backing. If anything goes wrong – you're on your own. . . . The photographs and map that go with this tape may give you a lead. Good luck."

"And we'll need it," said Jim Phelps, rising to his feet. He picked up the spool from the tape-recorder, aware that the very act of playing it through had already erased the secret message from its surface.

He glanced at the faces of his fellow agents, who were sitting around the table in his apartment.

"Do we take the job, then?" It was more of a rhetorical question. He hardly waited for their chorus of agreement, before opening the map that he had taken from an envelope.

"The underwater pod must be about here," said Barney. His forefinger came down where the light-blue shading of the continental shelf merged with the darker blue of deeper fathoms.

"Not the kind of place you can sneak into without being seen," said Willy drily. Cinnamon giggled.

6

schedule, then you might be able to walk in without suspicion, Rollin."

There was a moment's silence as they all weighed up the plan. The disguise expert nodded slowly. He looked towards Barney. "Can you tap into the 'hot line' to the pod?"

The corners of his companion's lips flickered in a swift smile. "It's been done before," was all he said.

Jim rubbed his hands and began to gather up the map. "Then what are we waiting for?" he demanded. "Let's get going for Katimura, huh?"

A huge overhead fan was stirring the sluggish, smoke-laden air inside 'Le Bar Orientale'. Cinnamon wrinkled her shapely nose in disgust at the stale odours that drifted through the crowded cellar. It was furnished with small tables, a horseshoe bar, and a tiny stage on which a native 'pop' group was grimly bashing out a tuneless jangling.

"Did we have to come here?" Cinnamon asked her companion.

Jim Phelps grinned, and filled up her glass from a bottle of wine. "It's not exactly the Statler-Hilton cocktail lounge," he agreed, "but we had to start looking for Grapler's family somewhere, and this is about the liveliest spot in Katimura."

Cinnamon sipped her drink. "I would describe it as the deadliest – not the liveliest," she cracked.

But Jim was not listening. His attention was drawn to an alcove not far away. Two thick-set men sat at a table there. They were drinking liquor, but did not seem to be having much fun. Both stared morosely across the heads of the half-drunken sailors who jostled and danced on the cellar floor, or sprawled at their tables.

"Not exactly cheerful characters, are they?" he mused aloud.

Jim was looking up from one of the photographs he had been examining. "Barney, supposing you could get close enough to the pod, how difficult would it be to tap into the hull with a listening device?"

Barney's poker-face never moved a muscle at the startling plan. "Might be done," he admitted, "if you knew what to listen for."

Jim nodded. He turned and tossed the photograph in front of Rollin Hand. "No need to ask if you could make yourself up to look like this guy," he said.

The disguise expert studied the florid, thin-lipped face that stared from the glossy surface with hooded hawk-eyes. "Who is he?" he asked.

"Name is Sablo. Rebel leader. Came to power in the insurrection a year ago. Remember?"

"Oh, yes." This was Cinnamon. "Wasn't he nicknamed The Switch, from his habit of carrying a riding switch?"

"Right." Jim nodded. "Now, on the back of that picture is a tip-off that Sablo is due for a visit to the undersea pod in four days' time to see the first test of Grapler's new device. . . . If we could just get a message through to the pod to say that Sablo will be arriving a day or two ahead of

Cinnamon had sensed her leader's interest in the men, and was watching them closely. "They're both wearing the same kind of slacks and shirt – almost like a uniform," she said.

"Like a couple of policemen on plain-clothes duty," pondered Jim.

"Or a couple of guards filling in time between duties," said Cinnamon.

"Ah!" said Jim.

"Yes," murmured Cinnamon.

"And the Graplers will be under heavy guard, being such important hostages," he added.

"They're finishing their drinks and leaving," she warned. "Let's follow them, before the fumes of this dive knock me out."

The air was even hotter in the dark street, but at least it was spiced with the scent of the fruits that made up the chief export of Katimura.

The agents went on soft feet. The men before them swung along in step. They were heading away from the waterfront.

"Look well if they walk into police headquarters." murmured Jim.

But it was soon plain that the men were making for a more secret destination, for they plunged into a labyrinth of alleys that wound between warehouse buildings and bazaars.

As Jim stepped round a corner in pursuit of their quarry, he suddenly grabbed the girl by the arm and pulled her into the shadows. Ahead of them, a door was being opened, spilling golden light onto the mud street. Two more beefy men in just the same kind of slacks and shirt could be glimpsed. They bulked ominously in the open doorway, and the light glinted on their carbines.

Cinnamon and Jim edged forward as the men engaged in a low-pitched growl of conversation. It was only when two of the men began to disagree that the listeners were rewarded with one vital clue. . . . "I don't care what Grapler's wife says, we're not running round to get a tonic for her kids at this time of night. She'll have to wait till the morning."

The two agents melted into the shadows as the men they had followed took the carbines from the guards in the building. The off-duty men shouted a good-night, and strode off, passing within three feet of the Mission Impossible team.

"Looks like we hit the jackpot first time," whispered Jim.

"Do we move in now and rescue the Graplers?" asked Cinnamon.

"No. Too soon. Can't afford to stir up a security scare when Sablo is due to visit the undersea pod in the morning," replied Jim.

"That's if Barney was able to tape their line and pass them a phoney message," said Cinnamon.

Jim grunted in the darkness. "If anyone can do it, it's Barney. . ."

The tribute was well-deserved. At that moment Barney was un-clipping his telephone-tapping equipment from a cable in the dripping darkness beneath the timbers of a naval jetty.

He was smiling to himself. "Well, they bought that one okay," he thought. "It's 'all systems go' and roll out the red carpet for Sablo when he arrives tomorrow."

He hauled himself up the rotting supports to the top of the jetty. A few moments later, he was driving his hired car along the twisting coast road. At length, he switched off his lights before turning from the road along a narrow track through brush and jungle.

He stopped at a derelict hut. As the sound of his engine faded away, two shadows materialised beside the car.

"Everything go okay?" whispered Willy.

Barney got out of the car. "Just fine," he said. "They're expecting you at nine tomorrow morning, Rollin."

The other shadowy figure nodded. "Fine. I'm arriving alone, of course, posing as a business-

man?"

"That's it," said Barney. "And they'll take you straight into the undersea pod. They're ordering Grapler to advance the time of the test for his explosive device."

"Sounds good," remarked Willy. "Let's get inside and have some food. Then we'll check our diving gear."

"Oh, sure," said Barney, as he followed his companions into the hut. "When Steve Stockdale flies in tomorrow, the first thing he'll

do is go over our frogman gear."

Stockdale was the ace frogman who had often helped the Mission Impossible team in their exploits. He was an unassuming man who held a cluster of medals in his drawer back home ... medals awarded for his expert penetration of undersea defence systems in Europe, Japan and Korea.

Barney and Willy met him next day, an hour after they had observed Rollin – now expertly disguised as Sablo, the rebel leader – make his rendezvous with the men who were to take him to the pod.

Stockdale listened carefully to Barney as the agents drove him to a lonely cove. He nodded approval when the plan had been outlined. "Hm ... the chances are that there's some kind of underwater barricade around this pod," he mused.

"Just what we figured," agreed Willy. "That's why we sent for the expert."

Twenty minutes later, the three men were in a small boat, heading in the direction of the cruiser that acted as a 'mother ship' for the pod.

Having approached the area as close as they dared, they put out two sea-anchors, donned their gear and slipped into the water.

They swam in silence, though each was in touch by means of projected impulse radio.

At last, Steve Stockdale held his hand up. Ahead, in the gloom of the water, a trailing barricade of wire had loomed up.

Barney and Willy trod water while Stockdale swam up and down the mesh, examining it closely without laying a hand on it. His voice crackled over the radio link. "Electro-sensitised. One touch will raise the alarm on the cruiser."

"Then how do we get past it?" asked Willy.

"*Over* it!" replied Stockdale.

"Ever fooled around in a swimming pool, tossing someone into the air to let them splash back in the water?"

"You mean, you put your foot in someone's cupped hands and they fling you upwards?" said Barney.

"Right . . . I'll do the flinging. Come on, Willy. You first."

It worked beautifully. First Willy, then Barney did a neat somersault over the barrier.

"But what about you, Steve?" asked Barney over the radio.

Stockdale had already unslung a large satchel from his back. He took out a collapsed rubber balloon, and a device that looked like a large Roman Candle. "Gas tube," he explained. "I'm going to inflate this balloon and with any luck, I'll come sailing over the top, like you guys. . . . But watch your heads. I'll come down with a

crack when I deflate the balloon."

A few moments later, the three men were swimming underwater in the direction of the cruiser. Down they went. Willy spotted a pale, rounded shape below. His voice quickened with excitement as he alerted the others. "There's the pod!"

It lay like some huge submarine monster sprawling on the sea bottom. There were observation windows and searchlights in the side of the hull. "Better split up and take different parts of the hull to listen at," crackled Stockdale's voice.

They turned and swam in different directions. Each took from his satchel the listening device that Barney had devised for the operation. The magnetic end of the device clamped onto the metal hull, and magnified every sound from within.

The minutes ticked by into half an hour. Then Willy and Barney appeared over the side of the pod, waving excitedly to Stockdale.

"I've got it," rasped Willy's voice. "Rollin just tapped out a message that Grapler's explosive device is on the sea bed half a mile southeast. Grapler will be exploding it by remote control in twenty minutes."

"Then we haven't a minute to spare," said Stockdale grimly. "Let's go find it."

They swam swiftly away. Fortunately their tasks became suddenly simpler as Willy spotted a cable running along the sea bed in the same direction as they were heading. "That's the cable for exploding the device," he pointed out.

"Pity we can't just disconnect it," mused Stockdale.

"That would blow the whole

that only a few minutes remained for them to carry out the plan.

At last, they heard Barney utter a grunt of satisfaction. His voice crackled over the radio link. "Done it! Handle this device gently, Willy. But let's get clear fast."

The others needed no urging. With Grapler's device in the satchel, on Willy's broad back, the trio swam desperately away ...

BOOM!

The blast reached out after them like a giant fist. It hit them viciously from behind, sending them spinning. Their ears drummed with the tremendous pressure, and they began to black out ...

plan," chuckled Barney. "The idea is that they should *think* that their big bang has gone off according to plan."

Grapler's device lay, bulbous and menacing, at the end of the cable trail.

"What in thunder does it do?" grunted Stockdale, swimming gingerly close to the black metal sphere.

"Kills everything within miles around," said Willy grimly. "It's a biological massacre ... wipes the sea clean of all life around it. Horrible!"

Barney was already examining the deadly device.

"Can you disconnect it safely?" queried Stockdale over the radio.

"It'll take a bit of time," grunted Barney, reaching for the tools strapped to his thigh. "Get the mine ready to connect in its place."

Willy slipped off his satchel. Carefully, he took from it the sea-mine that Barney had prepared to take the place of Grapler's device. It would, they hoped, simulate the vibrations set up by the device, so that the instruments recording the explosion would report back to the pod that the test had been a success.

As Barney's fingers, made slow and clumsy by their underwater task, attacked the wiring, his companions watched anxiously. Checking their watches, they saw

The party of three men who had just landed from the undersea pod climbed into a military saloon car, to the accompaniment of much heel clicking and saluting.

As the car pulled away from the jetty, General Zarnoff, the officer in charge of the pod, turned with a smile to his guest. "Well, comrade Sablo! You are happy with the test of Doctor Grapler's amazing weapon?"

The other's florid face broke into a brief, thin-lipped smile. "It is a weapon that I must possess. Amazing! When we reach your villa, we must discuss terms, General."

"Ah, yes – but first we shall celebrate our success with a bottle of champagne, eh, Doctor?" He reached over to slap the shoulder of the captured scientist, who sat hunched up dejectedly.

Suddenly all three men were flung about the car as it swerved, then skidded to a violent halt. There was a warning rattle of gunfire outside, and someone reached in and dragged the driver from his seat.

"What – " General Zarnoff was hauling out his pistol as he roared: "An ambush! Quick, Sablo!"

Sablo responded with lightning speed. His open hand whirled sideways. The karate chop caught Zarnoff a choking blow across the windpipe. He crumpled to the floor of the car, gurgling like a fish out of water.

Rollin snatched up the pistol as the door beside him was wrenched open.

Willy peered inside and grinned. "Oh, I beg your pardon, comrade Sablo!" he mocked.

Rollin scowled. "Cut the jokes, and help the Doctor out of the car," he said. "He's been a prisoner inside that pod until today. They said they would never let him out of it until he completed a successful test."

But, as the agents helped the scientist from the car, he began to protest: "No . . . I dare not go with you . . . . they have my family . . . they will harm them."

Barney stepped forward, cradling an automatic carbine in his hands. "Don't worry, Doctor. Your family is waiting for you just down the road. . . . Two of our agents rescued them half an hour ago. . . . They're waiting in the plane that's going to fly us all back home."

With a sob of relief, Grapler allowed himself to be hurried to a waiting car.

When Zarnoff had recovered enough from Rollin's karate blow to stagger onto the road, he heard the hum of an aircraft, taking off nearby. It passed low over his head, then lifted over the sea with a triumphant roar – as if to signal the end of another Mission Impossible.

Jim Phelps, head of the Mission Impossible team, is a strong believer in the theory that 'if you're going to do a job, then to do it properly you need to know all there is to know about it'. And he doesn't mean just being able to accomplish a mission successfully either!

This tough test is one that any agent wishing to join the IMF must complete — all answers correct. It isn't easy, they would all tell you that, but how about having a go for yourself? You might even turn out to be a natural for Jim Phelp's Mission Impossible team!

HOW GOOD A SPY WOULD YOU MAKE?

1. Which country would you say had the largest spying organisation in the world?

ROSSIA

2. An agent sent on a dangerous mission often has to have a 'cover'. Do you know what this entails?

AN ALIAS (CODE-NAME)

3. One of the most up-to-date methods of transmitting messages is by the microdot method. Do you know how it works?

TINY PHOTO

4. Margaretha Gertrude Zelle was the real name of a famous woman spy. By what name was she better known?

MATA HARI

5. A woman often said to be among the greatest of all woman spies was Madame Richer or Richard, but she was better known by her nickname. Do you know what it was?

?

6. What is an *agent provocateur*?

?

7. All secret agents need to be expert in both judo and karate, and a swift judo blow is often all that is needed to put an enemy out of action for a while. Which parts of the body would you aim for to make such a blow successful?

ADAMS APPLE, GROIN, NOSE SOLAR PLEXIS

8. Does an enemy agent ever resort to homicide?

YES, WHEN PROVOKED OR THREATENED

9. Conditions often aren't ideal for camera work for the spy. How would you photograph documents under these conditions:
    (a) in total darkness (b) from half a mile away

INFRA RED *ZOOM LENS*

10. A laser beam can cut through any kind of metal, but do you know
    (a) its other uses in espionage (b) what the letters LASER stand for

MESSAGES RADAR

Rating:

Top Score of 36 points: IMF needs agents like you; you really know what spying is all about.

30–35 points: With a little homework, you could make a good spy yet.

20–29 points: Well, you might be alright for a general knowledge team, but IMF wouldn't have much use for you.

Below 20: Forget it! How would you like to be something nice and easy, like a bank clerk, a policeman, or a brain surgeon!

ANSWERS

1. Russia. 2 points.

2. An agent would have to change his name and appearance as much as possible. If spying in a foreign country, he would have to speak the language fluently, of course, and even such details as wearing clothes which either have been or appear to have been made in the same country have to be seen to. 4 points — if all correct. 2 points only — if you missed anything at all.

3. This process uses a special camera and film, which can reduce a normal sheet of writing paper to something like the size of a full stop. The tiny film can then be easily hidden until necessary. A projector is used to magnify the film to normal size. Scoring as for question 2.

4. Mata Hari. 2 points.

5. L'Alouette, which is French for 'the lark'. 2 points.

6. An agent is called this when he provokes someone to do or say something which he can use to his own advantage. 4 points.

7. The best places to aim for are the solar plexus, the Adam's apple and the base of the nose. If attacking from behind, an agent would deliver his blow to the small of the back. 4 points (deduct one point for each of the ones missed).

8. Only when absolutely necessary, and only when complete success is certain. 4 points (two points only, if the second half of the answer has been missed).

9. (a) with an infra-red camera 2 points. (b) with a telephoto lens 2 points.

10. (a) to transmit messages or in a radar-like capacity 2 points. (b) Light Amplified by Stimulated Emissions of Radiation. 4 points.

ROUND THE WORLD QUIZ

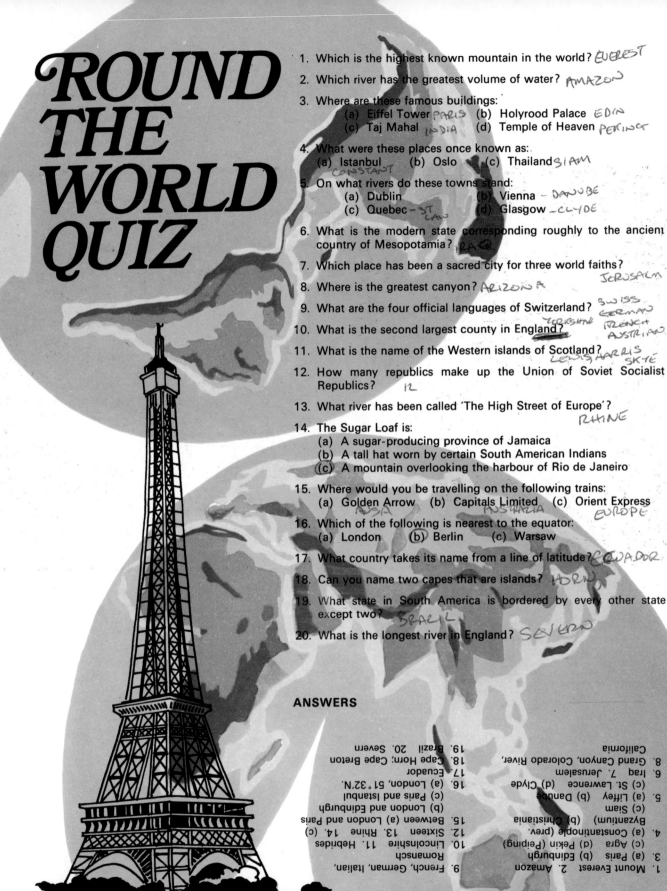

1. Which is the highest known mountain in the world? *EVEREST*

2. Which river has the greatest volume of water? *AMAZON*

3. Where are these famous buildings:
   (a) Eiffel Tower *PARIS*   (b) Holyrood Palace *EDIN*
   (c) Taj Mahal *INDIA*   (d) Temple of Heaven *PEKING*

4. What were these places once known as:
   (a) Istanbul *CONSTANT*   (b) Oslo   (c) Thailand *SIAM*

5. On what rivers do these towns stand:
   (a) Dublin   (b) Vienna – *DANUBE*
   (c) Quebec – *ST LAW*   (d) Glasgow – *CLYDE*

6. What is the modern state corresponding roughly to the ancient country of Mesopotamia? *IRAQ*

7. Which place has been a sacred city for three world faiths? *JERUSALM*

8. Where is the greatest canyon? *ARIZONA*

9. What are the four official languages of Switzerland? *SWISS GERMAN FRENCH AUSTRIAN*

10. What is the second largest county in England? *YORKSHIRE*

11. What is the name of the Western islands of Scotland? *LEWIS HARRIS SKYE*

12. How many republics make up the Union of Soviet Socialist Republics? *12*

13. What river has been called 'The High Street of Europe'? *RHINE*

14. The Sugar Loaf is:
    (a) A sugar-producing province of Jamaica
    (b) A tall hat worn by certain South American Indians
    (c) A mountain overlooking the harbour of Rio de Janeiro

15. Where would you be travelling on the following trains:
    (a) Golden Arrow *ASIA*   (b) Capitals Limited *AUSTRALIA*   (c) Orient Express *EUROPE*

16. Which of the following is nearest to the equator:
    (a) London   (b) Berlin   (c) Warsaw

17. What country takes its name from a line of latitude? *ECUADOR*

18. Can you name two capes that are islands? *HORN*

19. What state in South America is bordered by every other state except two? *BRAZIL*

20. What is the longest river in England? *SEVERN*

ANSWERS

1. Mount Everest 2. Amazon
3. (a) Paris (b) Edinburgh (c) Agra (d) Pekin (Peiping)
4. (a) Constantinople (prev. Byzantium) (b) Christiania (c) Siam
5. (a) Liffey (b) Danube (c) St. Lawrence (d) Clyde
6. Iraq 7. Jerusalem
8. Grand Canyon, Colorado River, California
9. French, German, Italian, Romansch
10. Lincolnshire 11. Hebrides
12. Sixteen 13. Rhine 14. (c)
15. Between (a) London and Paris (b) London and Edinburgh (c) Paris and Istanbul
16. (a) London, 51°32′N.
17. Ecuador
18. Cape Horn; Cape Breton
19. Brazil 20. Severn

16

KNOW YOUR SPORTS

1. This man scored 36 runs in one six-ball over, the highest score for one over ever recorded in first class cricket. Who is he, and which county does he represent?

2. Who scored England's second goal in the 1966 World Cup Final against West Germany at Wembley, and which football league club does he belong to? MARTIN PETERS, SPURS

3. The first open tennis tournament was held at Wimbledon in 1968. This woman won the women's singles championship for the third consecutive year. Who is she, and who was her opponent in the final? BJK.

4. On April 15th, 1967, at a Rugby Union match in Cardiff Arms Park, Keith Jarret equalled a 57-year-old record. What was the record, and how many times had Keith represented his country before this match?

5. Bob Beamon won the men's long jump at the Mexico Olympics in 1968. What distance did he jump? 29 FEET 2½ INCHES

6. Manchester United beat Benfica to win the 1968 European Club Champions Cup. What was the score, and who were the scorers?

ANSWERS

1. Garfield Sobers, the Nottinghamshire captain.
2. Martin Peters. Spurs.
3. Billie Jean King beat Anne Jones.
4. Jarret scored 19 points on his debut for Wales against England.
5. 29 ft. 2¼ ins.
6. Manchester United 4 (Charlton 2, Best, Kidd), Benfica 1 (Graca).

THE BIG HEIST

"So we're supposed to kill two birds with one stone, eh?" asked Barney.

"Right." Jim Phelps scattered more crumbs for the eager pigeons that strutted round the park bench. "This job breaks down into two parts – firstly, to guard the gold reserves in the Embassy vaults, since both the rival rebel leaders are planning to get their hands on it. And, secondly, to discredit both groups of insurrectionists."

"That's a fancy name for rebels, ain't it?" wisecracked Barney. "How many of them are there?"

Jim shrugged. "Oh . . . four, five hundred on each side," he said. "Vagrurra is one leader, and Impho the other. And they hate each other."

Barney held out his hand, palm upward with crumbs on it, and two pigeons fluttered onto it. "Oh well, it's about our usual odds in Mission Impossible, I guess – four guys against a thousand!" he said.

Jim grinned. He stood up and stretched himself, glancing round the green lawns of the city park. "Come on, let's get back to Headquarters. Cinnamon and Rollin will be waiting. We've got to fill them in on the job, and get a plan worked out."

Half an hour later the four agents were sitting round the table at Mission Force headquarters.

When their task had been outlined, Cinnamon arched her slender eyebrows and said: "The trick would seem to be to play one side against the other."

"You've hit it, Cinnamon," enthused Jim, snapping his fingers. "How would it be if *we* took Vagrurra's bunch, and Barney and Rollin took Impho's lot?"

"Okay. . . . but isn't there a snag? Who takes care that nobody breaks into the Embassy vaults and snatches the gold?" quizzed Rollin.

"Nobody." Jim let them chew over this surprising news, then added: "We *help* them to break in!"

The others exchanged glances of surprise. "We help them?" echoed Cinnamon. "Tell me more."

Jim was enjoying their puzzlement. He winked at Cinnamon. "Oh, you have quite a big hand in helping Comrade Vagrurra, my sweet," he told her. Then his tone became brisk and businesslike as he leaned towards them over the table. "Here's the plan. The Embassy vaults are practically impossible to crack – reinforced concrete, steel lining, doors a mile thick, sensitized floor – all the security refinements. . . . So I'm going to seek out Vagrurra, posing as an international crook who has been studying the layout and has a scheme for getting at the gold. . . ."

Carefully, Jim Phelps went over every detail of his idea, and then turned to the part that Barney and Rollin would play.

The same evening found Jim driving a low-slung Alfa-Romeo sports car along the coast road to the hills. The agent leader had changed into a flashy suit and panama hat, which went well with the expensive car.

The road turned inland and soon became a treacherous hairpin ascent. Jim drove with careless ease. The tyres screamed their protest at every bend.

Suddenly there was a rattle of gunfire. Jim grunted his satisfaction as he spotted a fallen tree rolled onto the road ahead, and glimpsed the gunmen who had fired the warning shots. He braked to a halt.

Without a word he jumped to the ground, and held up his arms so that the rebels could frisk him. Satisfied, they blindfolded him, bundled him into a car and drove away.

For half an hour they bounced over rough tracks. Then they halted. Jim was pulled from the car. His blindfold was removed. He saw that he was in a heavily-wooded ravine that had been turned into a hideout for rebel troops.

From the number of guards around the hut towards which he was now marched, Jim guessed that it was the headquarters of Vagrurra himself.

The rebel leader was a dapper man of middle height. He was studying a map, but paused to shoot a searching glance at the prisoner. "You were driving up the hill road," he purred in a silky tone. "Did nobody warn you that it would lead you to Vagrurra?"

Jim leaned on the desk. "Sure they did," he said. He let the words sink in, as his fingers slipped a tiny homing device out of sight beneath the edge of the desk.

"But then I've got a business deal to discuss with you."

Vagrurra lost interest in the map. He frowned angrily at the stranger's coolness. "What do you mean?" he demanded.

Jim straightened up. "You want to bust open the Embassy vaults. I know how it can be done," he announced.

The men around him stirred and murmured at the cool audacity of his words.

Vagrurra's glance was still hostile. "Who are you?" he demanded.

One of the rebels who had searched Jim now tossed his passport onto the desk.

Vagrurra picked it up. Jim noted the start of surprise that came as he opened the fake passport. "You are *the* Ivann Blinsk?" said Vagrurra.

"If you mean the top safe-cracker in the States – that's me!" said Jim.

"And how do you know I want to break into the Embassy vaults?" demanded the other.

For answer, Jim moved a hand to dip into his inside pocket. One of the guards jabbed a gun into his ribs.

Jim winced. "I just want to get some photographs," he protested.

The rebel leader waved his permission, and Jim took out several pictures which he put on the desk.

Vagrurra frowned at what he saw. "These are shots of my agents watching the Embassy building," he purred. "You are very clever, Mr. Blinsk."

"Just call me Ivann," said Jim, expansively. "Now, as soon as I found you were casing the joint, it occurred to me that we might do a deal."

Vagrurra watched him warily. "Go on," he invited. "What is this 'deal'?"

Jim sat on a corner of the desk and leaned towards the other man. "Well, you've got the men and the guns, I've got the way to get into those vaults. That gold bullion is worth three million if it's worth a penny. Suppose we settle for a million as my share, huh?"

Vagrurra leaned back in his chair. A gleam of interest was evident in his keen eyes. "First I would like to know your plan to enter the vaults," he said. "You realise, of course, that it is made of reinforced concrete, with sensitized floors, doors that are impossible to cut through –"

"And a lock that is operated by sonic vibrations," put in Jim.

Vagrurra gave a start of surprise. "You are remarkably well informed," he said.

Jim shrugged. "Of course. I also know that the Embassy is planning a big fancy dress ball there tomorrow night. They're planning some entertainment for the guests, and I can fix it so they hire a – er – friend of mine. She's an American night-club entertainer called Luna Laguna. A real dishy blonde . . . and you know what a weakness the President has for blondes!" Jim closed his eye in a knowing wink and grinned.

A thin smile hovered round the lips of the rebel leader. He leaned forward. "Ah . . . yes. I begin to see what your plan is," he admitted. "Your – er – Miss Laguna might be able to charm the President into letting her hear the sonic signal with which he opens the vault, eh?"

Jim spread his hands. "Exactly! And she'll have a midget tape-recorder picking up the key signal . . . . Brilliant, eh?"

Vagrurra pondered, frowning. "Enterprising, yes," he allowed. "But does your plan go any further? What about the difficulties of getting past the guards when we want to use the key?"

Jim gave a short laugh. "You

think I haven't got it worked out in every detail? They don't call me the King of Safebreakers for nothing, you know! Listen –" he leaned close to the rebel leader and murmured: "Luna will accidentally leave her vanity-bag on a ledge, behind the curtains in the Embassy. In it there's a small container of stun-gas timed to start releasing exactly two hours after Luna leaves. That will

take care of every security guard in the building."

Vagrurra purred with pleasure. "Excellent, Ivann!" he applauded. "I like the plan . . . . Indeed, as you Americans put it, you have a deal!"

Cinnamon was taking lunch in her hotel suite when Jim knocked at the door. She hurriedly slipped on a blonde wig that almost completely transformed her appearance, before calling: "Come in!"

Keeping up his disguise as Ivann Blinsk, the agent breezed into the room with a loud cry: "Luna, honey! How's show biz?"

But as Cinnamon closed the door he dropped the pretence, and grinned. "Vagrurra fell for it!" he said.

"Good," said the girl. "Now, all you've got to do is get me that booking at the Embassy Ball."

"Oh, don't worry! I've already fixed that," Jim assured her. "The rest is up to you. . . . And, I don't think you'll have much trouble sweeping the President off his feet, and getting him to play you his sonic vault-key. You look, *mmm* . . . real glamorous!"

Cinnamon laughed at the compliment. "Thanks. I hope you're right," she said. "But I wonder how Barney and Rollin are making out with Impho and his rebels?"

The other two agents were at that moment outlining to Impho their plan for cutting through to the Embassy vault from an adjoining building.

Impho was exactly the opposite of his rival rebel-leader. He was a huge man, fat but tough, with a completely bald head and a patch over one eye. He did not seem over-enthusiastic about the break-in plan.

"Ha . . . you call yourselves two professional safe crackers?" he boomed. "Don't you realise that as soon as you cut through into the vault – *if* you could ever do it – then the alarms would go off! That floor is sensitized. Once the vault is locked, anything heavier than a grain of dust touching the floor makes the bells go off."

Rollin chewed at the end of his

22

cigar. "Let's fill you in about our equipment, eh?" he said. "We use a laser torch with a high jet-stream of super-cooled air fired to a point just below the cutting cone. That means that as soon as the cut is made, the molten metal is solidified. It doesn't run and drip on the floor. Got me?"

Rollin was playing the part of a crook to perfection. Even Barney was impressed.

He tried to sound just as tough and assured as he took up the details of the plan: "And as for the problem of walking on the floor once we get in the vault, well – just watch this, Impho!"

He reached into a bag and took out a device like a sawn-off rifle. It had a rod-mounted, circular, magnetic clamp at one end.

Barney put the rifle to his shoulder and looked round. The walls of Impho's hideout were armour-plated in sections. He took aim at one of the metal walls and fired. The magnetic disc, trailing a pulley with a double length of nylon line, shot out and clamped close, as strongly as a limpet.

Without a word, the two agents then attached the free ends of the double line, and lashed them to a stanchion that supported the ceiling. Barney gave a couple of sharp tugs on the line, to make sure it would bear his weight. Then, hand over hand, he swung across the room, his feet swinging

inches away from the floor.

Impho uttered a growl of laughter. "Hey, that's good, boys!" he applauded. "Okay, you got all the help you need for this job. And I'll see you get a good cut of the bullion."

Jim Phelps, alias Ivann Blinsk, had been standing for half an hour with a crowd of curious onlookers gathered outside the Embassy to listen to the sounds of the ball, and watch the parade of important guests.

He knew that everything depended on Luna Laguna. Until she had played her part, his plan was at a standstill. He edged closer to the building. A broad-shouldered guard motioned him back with his rifle. There were guards everywhere.

But Jim was close enough to the side windows to glimpse the scene inside. And suddenly he saw Cinnamon.

She was an eye-catching figure in a low-cut white gown that shimmered with pearl trim. She was leaning on the arm of the President, and resting her blonde head provocatively on the gold-braid epaulette of his military uniform.

Above the faint sound of the orchestra, Jim heard her gay laugh echo from the open window.

The couple sat down at a seat near the window. Cinnamon reached into her vanity-case for a cigarette. Finding an empty packet, she tossed it through the open window. . . .

Jim was expecting that. He saw the packet land on a flower-bed. Waiting until the guards were busy pushing the spectators further from the Embassy, he sprinted forward and picked up the packet. . . .

A few moments later he was in the back of one of the plain trucks that Vagrurra had prepared for the bullion heist.

The rebel leader watched the 'crook' open the cigarette packet, and take out the midget tape. He slipped it into a recording machine, and thumbed the button. *Oooh . . . eeeh . . . aaah!* The sonic signal sounded something like a flautist tuning his instrument.

Jim and Vagrurra exchanged grins of satisfaction. "Good for Luna!" enthused 'Ivann'. "Here's the key to three million in gold!"

"Yes," agreed Vagrurra. "All goes well. . . . I have a man with a walkie-talkie watching to see when your friend leaves the ball. After that we shall be ready to move in."

Jim had to admire Vagrurra's efficiency in planning the transfer of the heavy gold bars from vault to trucks. Teams of men in government-style overalls were hidden in every truck, with trolleys and ramps.

It was not long before the signal was radioed from the watcher outside the Embassy. "The girl has left with the President in his car!"

Jim checked his watch. "Quarter after midnight is zero hour," he said. "Let's hope Luna managed to plant that stun-gas bomb!"

In the wine-cellar of a restaurant, in the building adjoining the Embassy, Barney and Rollin were working in grim, professional silence as they attacked the wall. The harsh whine of the heavy-duty masonry saw went on without a halt for an hour . . . two hours. . . .

They took it in turns to cut through the brickwork of the heavy wall, and each wore a mask.

"Steel plate," said Barney at length. "We've reached the Embassy vault. . . . Get the laser gear ready."

Rollin was already assembling the torch.

Suddenly there was a noise behind them. "Stop that!" It was Impho's voice. They pushed

back their masks and stared up into his angry face. "We're too late. My men have already spotted Vagrurra's men loading up the bullion in trucks at the front door of the Embassy. They've beaten us to it, you idiots!"

Barney ripped off his mask in a show of disgust and rage. "Those rats!" he blurted. "Couldn't you get your men and grab their trucks?"

"It would take an hour to get enough men here," snarled Impho. "And by now the trucks will have driven off, and nobody knows where Vagrurra has his hideout."

"*I* do!" declared Rollin. He had a look of murderous hate on his face.

"You do?" growled Impho. "How?"

Rollin's lip curled. "Because we took our plan to Vagrurra, and he turned it down," he lied glibly.

Barney chuckled inside himself at the conviction his partner put into this pretence.

"Yeah, that's right," said Barney. "And now it seems you'll have a chance to get the gold without any trouble, and wipe out the opposition at the same time."

Impho grunted and frowned. Then, as the truth of the remark came home, he began to brighten. "Hm . . . you're right. They'll be busy unloading the bullion, and celebrating their big heist," he mused. "We could move in fast, wipe out any opposition, get the rest of his men to join my troops, and still have the gold."

Rollin was on his feet, grabbing the cutting gear and stowing it away. "What are we waiting for?" he demanded. "Come on. Call out your men, and have them follow us in our car."

It was a convoy without lights that wound its way up the zigzag mountain road.

Barney, at the wheel of the car, glanced in his rear-view mirror at the dark shapes of Impho's troop vehicles crawling upwards. "How much further?" he asked.

Rollin was seated beside him. On his knee was a small electronic device that was picking up the signals from the homing device that Jim had planted under Vagrurra's desk. The *peep-peep-peep* from the machine had been growing steadily louder.

"Pull off the road at the next bend," said Rollin.

The convoy halted and the rebel troops dismounted and assembled silently on the road.

Rollin was pointing the way to Impho. "About half a mile in that direction," he said.

As the rebel leader turned to command his troops, Barney hissed: "What about giving us guns? We've got a score to settle too, y'know."

Impho's lip curled in contempt. "You stick to your safe cracking, boys," he sneered. "Leave the fighting to us."

Barney watched the rebel force vanish into the shadows on the hillside. Then he chuckled quietly. "Well, we set them at each others throats, so now we'd better get clear before the Government troops show up to pick up the pieces."

They drove back down the mountain road at a fast clip. At a rendezvous on the outskirts of the town they met Jim and Cinnamon. She had discarded her blonde wig, but still wore the glamorous dress.

"Too bad I had to ditch the President, after our short, romantic attachment," she sighed.

"You did a marvellous job," said Jim. "And you too, boys."

They paused to listen to the rattle of distant gunfire in the hills. Then, out of town and up the mountain road, came pouring the armoured vehicles of the Government troops.

It was Barney who put their thoughts into words: "Mission completed. . . . We've made sure the Embassy gold goes back to its vault, *and* I guess we might say both groups of rebels are – er – discredited. Right?"

SOON...

IT'S UP TO YOU, BARNEY, TO GET IN CLOSE, POSING AS ONE OF THE LOCALS.

..AND I'LL BE READY TO STAND BY WITH THE HELICOPTER.

RIGHT! WILLIE AND I WILL BE READY TO FOLLOW BARNEY IN.

MEANWHILE...

HELLO! I THOUGHT I SAW SOMEONE MOVING DOWN THERE.

HMM! ONLY ONE OF THE LOCALS GOING ABOUT HIS BUSINESS.

TEUFEL! WHA---?

MEANWHILE...

RIGHT! BARNEY SHOULD BE THROUGH PRETTY SOON. LET'S GO!

JIM AND WILLIE REACH THE CAVE.

NOT A GUARD IN SIGHT, JIM.

INSIDE...

YOU TWO RELIEVE THE SENTRIES. I'LL TAKE A LOOK AT LEMAN.

I HOPE JIM AND WILLIE ARE IN POSITION.

THE TWO RELIEF SENTRIES LEAVE THE CAVE...

HELLO! WHERE'S STEIGER?

HE'S PROBABLY GONE TO SPEAK TO KURTZ.

SUDDENLY...

MAKE IT SHORT AND SHARP, WILLIE!

LOOK OUT, HANS!

SECONDS LATER...

LET'S HOPE MARC IS O.K.

THE CELL DOOR SWINGS OPEN AND...

COME ON, MARC! I'VE JUST DECLARED AN AMNESTY.

LEAD ON, MACDUFF! I WAS BEGINNING TO GET A BIT BORED.

MARC DASHES THROUGH THE TUNNEL FOLLOWED BY BARNEY AS THE GUARDS OPEN FIRE, BUT JIM AND WILLIE TAKE A HAND...

AAH!

SOON...

ALL ABOARD, BOYS! LET'S NOT HANG ABOUT!

CINNAMON'S THERE, BANG ON TIME

AND BANG ON THE BUTTON!

NICE WORK, CINNAMON!

NEAT TIMING ALL ROUND.

BAH! THEY'VE GOT AWAY! WE'VE FAILED!

POSSIBLE WORDS

Clues Across:

2. A tin one, perhaps?
6. You can get either film or dots
7. This calms troubled waters
8. Water that's been frozen
9. A kind of grass
10. Playing . . . . sometimes gets results.
13. Something that makes the day brighter
14. Basic equipment of any special agent
15. An undercover spy's name is probably one of these
18. A small Scottish deer
19. It's always better to do this than to lose
21. Midday
22. Initials of the espionage forces
23. Spying is certainly never this
24. The opposition
28. A fragrant substance sometimes used in perfume
30. Headquarters
31. A requirement
32. A famous female spy's surname

Clues Down:

1. The current passed between two carbon points
2. A secret way of relaying messages
3. A Mission Impossible agent
4. Spies are often sent on one
5. A famous female spy in the IMF
6. The abbreviation of *over*
10. Another IMF agent
11. Spring into action without any more of this
12. A Biblical term meaning look
16. Another name given to a spy
17. One of the first places where a spy might look
20. Good often comes before this
25. Famous female spy's first name
26. Special agents often have to carry one of these
27. Make something last longer
29. The direction in which a spy could be sent

ANSWERS

Across: 2. Can; 6. Micro; 7. Oil; 8. Ice; 9. Rye; 10. Ball; 13. Sun; 14. Radio; 15. Alias; 18. Roe; 19. Gain; 21. Noon; 22. EF; 23. Easy; 24. Enemy; 28. Musk; 30. HQ; 31. Need; 32. Hari.

Down: 1. Arc; 2. Code; 3. Willie; 4. Mission; 5. Cinnamon; 6. Oer; 10. Barney; 11. Ado; 12. Lo; 16. Agent; 17. Safe; 20. Bye; 25. Mata; 26. Gun; 27. Eke; 29. SE (south east).

MISSION ACHIEVED!

Jim Phelps and his team always manage to complete a seemingly impossible mission successfully. But, down through the ages, others have also achieved their goal, against what appeared to be overwhelming odds. Do you know:

1. Which Carthaginian general crossed the Alps with a herd of elephants? *HANNIBAL*

2. Which three men succeeded in holding the bridge over the river Tiber against a whole army?

3. By what means the Greeks entered Troy, and by what similar ruse three prisoners escaped from a German camp during World War II? *WOODEN HORSE*

4. Who were the first two men to fly across the Atlantic? *WRIGHT BROS.*

5. Who was the missionary who brought a large band of refugee children safely out of enemy-occupied China?

6. Who succeeded in cutting off the Gorgon's head? *HERCULES*

7. Who crossed Niagara Falls on a tightrope, blindfolded, and pushing a woman in a wheelbarrow?

8. What was the name of the young girl who rowed out one stormy night to rescue the passengers of the *Forfarshire* when it was wrecked off the Northumbrian coast?

9. Who was given a free pardon even though he was caught stealing England's Crown Jewels?

10. A Greek messenger named Pheidippides ran one hundred and fifty miles to Sparta to ask for help, and then ran the same distance back to Athens. His wonderful achievement is remembered at each Olympic games. What is this race called? *MARATHON*

ANSWERS

1. Hannibal.
2. Horatius Cocles; Spurius Lartius; Titus Herminius.
3. Inside a wooden horse.
4. John William Alcock and Arthur Whitten Brown.
5. Gladys Aylward.
6. Perseus.
7. Blondin.
8. Grace Darling.
9. Captain Blood.
10. The Marathon.

Jim Phelps took the tape from the recorder and held it above the waste-disposal unit in the room of his apartment that he uses as an office.

It began to smoulder, then burst into white smoke and flared to extinction. He dropped it and looked round at his staff with a wry face. "We've just been handed the most impossible task we've ever undertaken," he said with a dry smile. He pressed the red button on his desk which would notify those who had sent the taped instructions that he accepted the job. "The usual rigmarole about 'if we accept' (as though we ever refused) and that final benediction as to their bland disavowal of our very existences in the event of failure."

CODENAME— SCAPEGOAT

"Our revered and mysterious bosses," said Rollin Hand sarcastically, "always play it the 'Fail-Safe' way."

Cinnamon said nothing but touched her red hair. They all waited in silence for his words.

"On the surface, dead easy," he began. "Seems like a piece of cake. But in reality it'll be as rugged as they come. The Chairman of the Federation of Eastern Broznia is coming to Washington incognito!"

"Impossible, for a start," said Barney, elaborately filing his nails. "If that bird ever moves from his eagle's nest in the Caucasus, he brings about half his security boys with him. Like a small army."

"Not this time, Barney," Jim said. "This time he comes in a single T.U. 104, with no escort planes. He'll have guards on the jet, but that will be all. He is scheduled to land at Kennedy Airport inside forty-eight hours. That's been released; no use trying to keep that secret in the world we have today of instant international communication. But our top brass has given me the real dope. His jet is really due to put down at Chicago in *twenty-four* hours, a day ahead of the scheduled New York landing. As far as can be known, this is the real secret."

They all waited, knowing that Jim would bring the whole story out in his own way and in his own time. They asked no questions; I.M.F. staff never did.

"The Oriental Federation are going to kidnap our Broznian friend as soon as his aircraft lands anywhere *en route*. It isn't scheduled to land anywhere as it comes high over the Pole but—"

"Why kidnap Alexei Arenzov?" asked Cinnamon. "He's just one man. The real rulers of the Federation of Eastern Broznia are a praesidium of thirteen members. Since the days of Vassili Karovny, there hasn't been one-man rule."

Jim Phelps smiled. "So the world thinks, Cinnamon, but it isn't true. This Arenzov is a new kind of man. He *is* Broznia, and he is supreme in a way that even Karovny wasn't dictator of his country. With Arenzov out of the way, Broznia falls into disarray for just long enough for the Orientals to strike and move in. You can guess what that'd mean. For the peace of the world, we have to stop this kidnapping attempt, at all costs. We, as always, are expendable. The Orientals will stop at nothing. You remember the Kamikazis of Japan in the last war? The 'Divine Wind' pilots, and their suicide missions? Well, we have to be Kamikazis for a few hours. In fact, we have to be three Kamikazi groups."

"Three?" said Rollin Hand, and Jim nodded gravely.

"During the next twenty-four hours," he said soberly, "we have to be in three places at once. We have to be at Kennedy Airport, at Chicago's Soldier Field, and in Iceland. The latest from Central Intelligence Agency is that Arenzov's plane *will land* at Reykjavik. So we have to split our forces three ways. Partly in Chicago, partly in New York, and partly in Iceland."

"As there are just five of us here," observed Cinnamon dryly, "that's going to be the most impossible part of this mission.

What about the Central Intelligence Agency and the Federal Bureau of Investigation? Are they all on vacation or something?"

"The C.I.A. and the F.B.I.," said Jim evenly, "aren't being let into this one. Far too delicate even for them. The rest of the world isn't to know even that a snatch is anticipated, let alone what is being done about it."

"One more thing," put in Willy woodenly. "Why should the President and the Chairman go to such extravagant, comic-opera lengths just to meet each other? What about the 'hot line'?"

"Here's something we *have* been told and must at once *forget*," said Jim. "The 'hot line' is no longer secret. It's been tapped by the Orientals!"

That news stunned them all for a little while. The peace of the whole globe had often depended on the direct link between the President and the Broznian leader.

"Barney, you're for Chicago," said Jim Phelps. "Cinnamon, you and Willy are for Kennedy Airport. Rollin, it's you and I for Iceland. Get out your thickest furs."

"Which of us draws the jackpot, d'you think, Jim?" asked Hand composedly. Jim Phelps shrugged. "That's up to chance and our Oriental brothers. Literally anything can happen at any one of the three key-points."

Cinnamon and Willy left at once for New York, and Barney for Chicago. Jim and Rollin were left, and before they went, Jim gave Rollin a cellophane envelope and took one for himself. "We take our new identities with us," he said, and Hand asked no more questions.

The President had come from Andrews Air-Base at Washington, and the big jet, inscribed 'Air-Force One', stood in a remote part of Soldier Field as Barney arrived.

His credentials got him through the massed ranks of guards and, with his camera, he joined the horde of pressmen held back by F.B.I. men.

The President landed and was whisked away to a V.I.P. lounge, and Barney got his photographs; it really was the Chief himself, all safe and sound. It was a stop of only a half-hour and then Barney saw the Presidential party again board Air-Force One and the plane take off for New York.

Barney shrugged. His part of the project seemed to have been the easiest. He flew back at once to H.Q. and relaxed beside the radio communicators. Jim might be paging him at any moment.

Inside five seconds, Rollin was staring into the face of the President of the U.S.A. and when he donned his own flesh-mask and looked in a mirror, he saw that he had miraculously become the Chairman of the Broznian Federation.

"I'm asking no questions, Jim," he said quietly.

"Just as well," grunted Jim. "I don't have any answers. But this is the drill, and from now on we play it by ear." He pulled the fur parka closer round his face, and together they went out into the lounge bar.

They were spotted as soon as they appeared and were immediately surrounded by security men.

"Mr. President," said their leader, "I must really ask you to be more careful. Forgive me, but if you will step into this lounge – you, too, Mr. Arenzov. Everything is ready for the conference."

"This way, Mr. Chairman," said Jim Phelps gravely, and he guided Rollin into the lounge round which the guards were massing. This was going to be good, he thought. So the Orientals were wise to the dodge, after all. The real meeting between the two most powerful men in the world was to take place here in Iceland, and not at New York, Chicago, or even Washington.

A double group of statesmen were awaiting them, Cabinet members from home and praesidium members from across the steppes.

The two I.M.F. men bowed gravely to them all and shook hands solemnly. There was a storm of clapping and the flashing of many bulbs as the carefully screened reporters and news comment people took their photos and had their moment.

Then the Secretary of State came forward and guided them both into an inner room. "You'll

Cinnamon and Willy never even saw the plane, for it winged its way in the stratosphere northwest for Iceland. It was left to Jim Phelps and Rollin Hand to take all the strain.

It was cold at Reykjavik and the pair were in the warm bar, keeping their distance from the Air-Force personnel and the security guards. For once, there wasn't a blizzard blowing and the windswept runways were cleared for the arrival of the Broznian jet.

It came out of the northern snow-clouds dead on schedule, and the guards sprang to attention. Now the two I.M.F. men slipped into the men's room and Jim took out his cellophane package. "This is it, Rollin," he said tensely.

be completely private and isolated here, gentlemen," he murmured. "This room has been specially built for this meeting and has been most thoroughly debugged. Not a fly could get inside."

Jim relaxed and helped himself to whisky. "There's vodka for you, Mr. Chairman," he grinned. "But maybe you'd rather stick to Bourbon?"

"Too true, Jim," said Rollin, frowning. "But I don't get the set-up. We can't carry on as President and Chairman. Where are the real men?"

"Not for us to ask," said Jim, and he relaxed into a deep arm-chair. "You and I have got to settle all the problems concerning two-thirds of the people in the world. Take about ten minutes, I'd guess."

Rollin Hand laughed a deep, sardonic laugh. "We're the stake-out or scapegoat, then? You did say a Kamikazi mission, I'll grant you that. But, what a way to go! We won't have a chance to say cheerio to the bunch."

"Something happening to the roof," said Jim casually. "Act naturally. I'd say it's our pals from the Orient. We go with them, but only part-way. Air-Force One and the T.U. 104 have their motors still turning. It shouldn't be long now."

They struggled a little, just enough for their captors to be certain that they were dealing with two elderly statesmen. Gags were put over their mouths and they were pulled to their feet.

A bland Oriental officer spoke. "A 'copter is coming to the roof,"

he told them. "It will take us to our jet. We are inviting you both to Peking, gentlemen. It is a singular privilege for you both. No harm will come to you, I assure you, for at least three days. After that . . . well, this is a very dangerous world, my friends, and we intend to make it a world in which neither of you, with your quaint philosophies of peace, would wish to live."

A square of the roof drew back and they heard the thrashing of a helicopter outside. They were hauled up and dumped into the machine. A fusillade of shots came from the security guards, but the 'copter darted in a zig-zag course over to a distant corner of the field. It landed on snow, and the two captives were nudged out.

Jim Phelps stared over the

thinly-covered snow. "Any minute now," he told himself, and he touched Rollin.

The thunder of jets from two separate corners of the runway complex told him that 'Air-Force One' and the Broznian jet were taking off. Voluntarily he went up into the Oriental plane and Rollin followed him. The jubilant kidnappers followed, and the door slammed. This plane too was idling its motors, and the three planes took off almost simultaneously. The Presidential jet was first away, due west. The Broznian plane went north-east and their prison plane took off for the Pole.

Jim grabbed out his gun and fired at the nearest window. Rollin, too, fired a fusillade, and presently even the stout windows shattered. Each dragged off his mask and plunged for the open windows.

The Orientals were firing rapidly and bullets were flying as the big jet was airborne. But both the I.M.F. men were out into the cold air again.

They dropped maybe fifty feet into snowdrifts and the jet roared on.

"They can't rise far without pressurisation," Jim said, as he helped Rollin to his feet and stared towards the distant runways. Lights were flashing and men were milling to-and-fro. Fire and ambulance tenders were ringing their bells and sounding their sirens.

"The two Big Boys will have made it by now," Jim said. "We can relax."

They were arrested by security guards as soon as they approached and were disarmed and taken into close custody. Phones brayed and radios buzzed, and a captain of Intelligence came to them. "Now, what's all this?" he

demanded. He stared at them closely. "Impossible Missions Force," he said. "No use to me. We've no electronic checker here. Now then, you two, what's the real story? You're from the Orient, I'd guess."

"Check with New York, Chicago, and Washington," Jim Phelps rapped out in a tone of command, and the officer winced. These men were a big mystery and he shivered a little. This whole thing was so off-beat. A guy never knew whom he was dealing with.

He moved to the radio in the hut. The operator handed him earphones and a mike and flipped the switches.

"Disturbances at New York and Chicago," said the captain slowly. "A man and a red-haired woman involved at Kennedy and a solitary coloured man at Chicago. They've been arrested, along with unidentified Orientals."

"The woman and man at New York," jerked Hand. "And the man at Chicago—are they injured? Come on, man, make enquiries. And get in touch with the White House at once."

"Yes, sir," said the captain humbly. He was in deeper waters than even he had imagined. He listened. "No casualties in Chicago or New York," he said. "From Washington – President's plane approaching Andrews Air-Base now. What goes on here, fellas? Tell a guy, can't you?"

"They never tell us anything, do they, chum?" grinned Jim Phelps. "Get a couple of nice, warm cells ready for us to sleep in, will you? None of our names will go down in history, I'm afraid. But it may be some comfort to you, Captain, to know that you and I and Rollin here, and the hundreds of men involved in this scapegoat stake-out, have postponed World War III, at least for the time being."

OPERATION RESCUE

START

CLUE TO SCIENTIST'S WHEREABOUTS FROM FILM OF KIDNAPPING. GO ON 2 SQUARES.

A top-flight nuclear scientist has been kidnapped during some riots in the country in which he was holidaying at the time. The Mission Impossible team have an assignment once again.

"Find that scientist!" The order was brief and to the point, and soon the team was speeding to a tiny country in South America, which had been the scene of the crime.

FIRST CLASH WITH ENEMY AGENTS, MISSION IMPOSSIBLE TEAM LOSE. GO BACK TO START.

THERE SEEMS TO BE SOME KIND OF MIX-UP HERE. MISS 1 TURN.

A BIT OF SMART THINKING SETS YOU ON THE RIGHT TRACK. GO ON 3 SQUARES.

AN ENEMY AGENT WHO HAS BEEN DRUGGED TURNS TALKATIVE. GO ON 3 SQUARES.

INFORMATION FROM A RELIABLE SOURCE. TAKE ANOTHER TURN

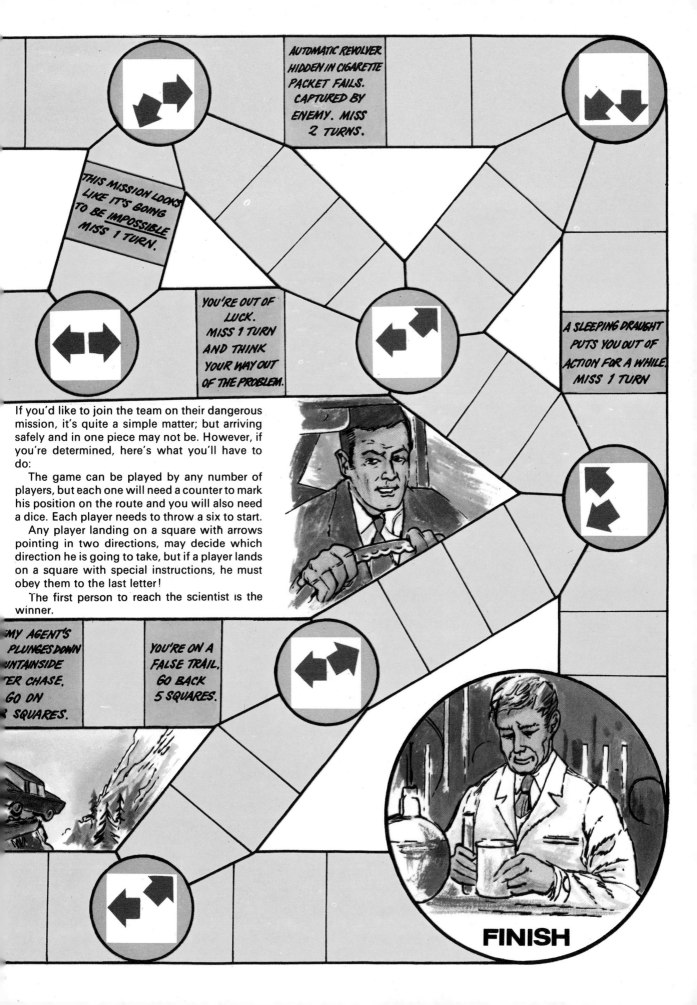

AUTOMATIC REVOLVER HIDDEN IN CIGARETTE PACKET FAILS. CAPTURED BY ENEMY. MISS 2 TURNS.

THIS MISSION LOOKS LIKE IT'S GOING TO BE IMPOSSIBLE. MISS 1 TURN.

YOU'RE OUT OF LUCK. MISS 1 TURN AND THINK YOUR WAY OUT OF THE PROBLEM.

A SLEEPING DRAUGHT PUTS YOU OUT OF ACTION FOR A WHILE. MISS 1 TURN

If you'd like to join the team on their dangerous mission, it's quite a simple matter; but arriving safely and in one piece may not be. However, if you're determined, here's what you'll have to do:

The game can be played by any number of players, but each one will need a counter to mark his position on the route and you will also need a dice. Each player needs to throw a six to start.

Any player landing on a square with arrows pointing in two directions, may decide which direction he is going to take, but if a player lands on a square with special instructions, he must obey them to the last letter!

The first person to reach the scientist is the winner.

MY AGENT'S PLUNGES DOWN MOUNTAINSIDE AFTER CHASE. GO ON SQUARES.

YOU'RE ON A FALSE TRAIL. GO BACK 5 SQUARES.

FINISH

DOUBLE TROUBLE

Jim Phelps went into the abandoned shed on the river bank and found the tape, as arranged, under a pile of old sacking. Crouching down, he threaded it into his pocket tape-recorder.

"Your mission, Jim," said the toneless voice from the tape, "should you decide to accept, is to intercept delivery of a vital part of the triggering device of a tritium bomb which the People's Republic of Orientalia has developed. The bomb itself can be carried in a brief-case. The President and his whole Cabinet, together with the Joint Chiefs of Staff, are meeting secretly in two days' time in the White House. The laboratory to which the device is to be delivered is in Greenwich Village. A man, who will give you his name as 'Jim Phelps', will contact you this night at Impossible Missions Force H.Q. If the device can be diverted, the bomb cannot be triggered. If it is, and the brief-case is inserted into the personal luggage of the men who will attend the meeting, it will follow that the Free West will be stripped, at one blow, of all its effective heads and we will be open to an all-out attack by Orientalia. Of course you know that if you accept this assignment and you or any member of your group is captured or killed, your Government will disavow any knowledge of your actions. You'll be on your own all the way. Good luck, Jim. This tape will self-destruct in five seconds."

Stolidly, Jim took the tape from the recorder and waited. A flare, a puff of white smoke, and the reel was empty. Getting to his feet, he left the hut.

"A ripe one this time, Jim," said Barney thoughtfully, after Jim had told his team the score. "Doubles, is it now? Two of Jim Phelps! Well, now I've seen everything. Anything we can do until this guy shows up?"

"Well, gentlemen," smiled Cinnamon, "we can at least relax over coffee. I'll brew up at once."

"We'll sketch out interim plans while we wait," said Jim. "You, Rollin, and you, Willy, will be at the South Gate to the White House. As the essence of our mission is that the meeting of the top brass know nothing of the coming attempt, it won't be possible for you to be given official status as members of the Security Forces. You'll be entirely on your own."

"That'll be nothing new," observed Willy placidly, and Rollin Hand said nothing. He very rarely did.

"Barney," went on Jim, "it's you and I for our visitor. You to the Greenwich Village laboratory, and myself to stick closer to our friend than his own skin."

"That leaves just little me," smiled Cinnamon, sipping coffee.

"At the moment, nothing," smiled Jim. "Except maybe comforts for the troops. But I've no doubt that before we're through, there'll be a slot for you, Cinnamon, upon which, as often happens, the ultimate success of the project will depend."

The man who gave his name to the door guard as 'Jim Phelps' arrived at ten that night. He was foreign, that was quite obvious, though his English was perfect. "I'm Jim Phelps," he began, and the real Jim laughed.

"Snap!" he said. "So am I. Where does that leave us?"

The stranger smiled. "It's all part of the plan," he explained. "My name, of course, is not really Jim Phelps at all. If I told it to you, you would never be able to

pronounce it. Playing it this way, we have two aces."

"Don't see that," Barney objected. "You two don't look alike one little bit. Could cause endless confusion, in my opinion."

"Exactly," was the reply. "It is precisely for that purpose that this was arranged." He was a thin, wiry, dark-haired fellow, and he looked with admiration at Jim Phelps. "I am just a lowly member of our organisation, Mr. Phelps, and they do me too much honour to let me use your name, which is, I might say, illustrious in the secret annals of I.M.F."

"Huh!" said Jim, and the others laughed.

"One Jim Phelps is great," went on the new man. "But two of the same name should ensure success. That is not to say that I would make any attempt at all to compare myself with the real holder of that name."

Smooth, thought Jim Phelps, very smooth. But the fellow had his credentials all above board. The orders had told of him being named 'Jim Phelps' and he had the correct card, which showed clear in the electronic scanner.

"We'll pass up the bouquets, shall we?" he said, a little stiffly. "We should get down to cases right away. We've less than two days. What's the set-up? I suppose you've information for us?"

The stranger looked round and saw the board on the wall. He took up a piece of chalk and began to make two sketches. The first was of the building in Greenwich Village where the laboratory was situated. This was exact and complete, and they all memorised it as the chalk flew over the board.

But when the artist began to sketch in the plan of the White House itself – from cellars to attics, all corridors, lifts, guard points, windows, even the very wiring diagram of the whole complex – Jim's respect for the new

44

man grew by leaps and bounds. This chap had said he was low in the echelon of I.M.F. This detailed knowledge, all in his head, of every inch of the Executive Mansion, betokened that this second 'Jim Phelps' must be very close to the very top shelf in the Force.

He broke in. "There's the laboratory in the Village and there's the White House," he said thoughtfully. "Why the two? Why don't we concentrate on the laboratory where this device, or trigger, or what-have-you, is to be delivered?"

"The 'Fail-Safe' method, Mr. Phelps," smiled the other. "We must be prepared for initial failure at the New York point. That we must take for granted. It is at the White House itself that your forces must concentrate. Now, as I said before, the duplication of Jim Phelps will ensure us success. Therefore—" He took from his pocket a small cellophane bag, and turned away. When he turned again, adjusting his hair-line and neck, the team were astonished to see an exact double of the real Jim Phelps, without a wrinkle in the mask.

"Even the voice has been thought of," he said, and Jim and the rest were uncannily surprised to hear the same tones, almost exactly like the real voice of their own leader.

"They certainly thought of everything," said Barney critically. "I can't make out which of you is the real article."

"If *you* can't," said the new man, "the other side won't be able to."

Jim Phelps stood beside Cinnamon, and she alone of them knew that he was the real one. "Right, now here's where we start. You and I will go to this laboratory—"

"Will you take my advice?" said the new man. "I would suggest that you, Mr. Phelps, go to the White House. I, whom we shall call X, will go to the laboratory with one of your team. I know these people with whom we are dealing. They will think I am Jim Phelps, of course, and that will give me my advantage. You, the real man, will be at the White House."

"Well," said Jim judiciously, "as we're playing it off the cuff, and you seem to know it all, I'll go along with that. I'll take your place, Willy, and stick with Rollin. Barney, you go with Mr. X. What are the signals?"

"No signals," said Mr. X. "Too dangerous. Barney here will be with me, and he will relay any messages."

"Quite a way from the Village, in New York, to Washington," commented Cinnamon. "Could be many a slip-up between the two points, I'd guess."

"There will be no slip-ups, dear lady," said Mr. X, bowing. "I assure you of that. Barney and I will be at the laboratory to see who it is that is carrying the brief-case containing the device."

Jim Phelps frowned. "You aren't going to attempt to hold it up, then? To me, that's like discarding an ace. We should make the attempt, and then, if that failed, we could concentrate on Washington."

"Ah!" smiled Mr. X. "You forget. As the lady says, it is a long way between the two crisis points."

Jim nodded soberly. He wasn't too pleased that this man was taking such an apparently decisive part in the mission. It left him, the real leader, in a somewhat odd position.

The dilapidated old building in Gramercy Park was big and dark as the car drove up.

Mr. X got out, followed by Barney. "Up that alley," muttered X, and Barney melted into the

shadows.

They went along the alley to the rear of the buildings, and then saw that one bright window shone, on the first floor. X pointed a finger.

In single file they climbed up the drain-pipe, and Barney crouched on the sill and pulled up the foreigner.

"The device is to be delivered at midnight, just about now," said X, in a hoarse whisper. "I know the way in. Wait here."

Barney waited and listened. Voices came from within, and they were in a language Barney could only partly understand. But what little he did hear made

him stiffen – it was Russian!

Then he relaxed. Obviously this man who called himself X could quite easily be a Russian defector. That would be why he knew so much of the inner workings of this thing. Still, it nagged at Barney's mind. He applied his eye to a slit in the blind.

What he saw almost made him fall from the sill. A briefcase on a table was being packed, and into it, in a cotton-wool cradle, was being placed a small, glittering mechanism of some kind. Barney knew the only thing that could be.

X was handling the thing delicately and lovingly. Barney heard

him chuckle to the other man in the room, a fellow in the uniform of the Federal Security Forces! Barney's eyes narrowed to slits. In the few words he picked up and could interpret, he knew that they were being tricked and that X, instead of being a higher-up in I.M.F., was in reality a double agent for Orientalia. Without another thought, he hurled himself at the window and went through in a shower of glass and clashing blind-slats.

The two men had guns out as he smashed in. X snapped shut the case and rapped to the other: "You take it. Plan B now. I'll deal with this fool." Without

speaking, the man grabbed the briefcase and darted from the door. X was already firing, but Barney wasn't ever in the path of the shells. His fingers were at the man's throat, and a bullet went through the lapel of his jacket. He squeezed and squeezed, and the man's form stiffened, then went slack until, like an empty sack, he fell to the floor.

Barney ripped the flesh mask from his face, grabbed the electronic identity card from the pocket, and darted to the window.

The car they had come in was vanishing up the square as he came out into Gramercy Park, and Barney's mouth closed like a

rat-trap. There'd be no chase tonight. First, he had to find a hire-car lot, and then. . . .

"Sorry, bud," said the stalwart guard at the South Gate of the White House. "We been warned against a guy with your likeness. Guess you'd oughter grown a moustache or something, to hide that pan of yours."

"You're making a great mistake, sergeant," said Rollin Hand curtly. "We cannot tell you who we are—"

The sergeant chuckled. "Secret agents, huh? G-Men, maybe. Baloney! We got word that a guy with your mug was working

for Orientalia as a double agent. And here you are, right into the rat-trap."

Jim Phelps stared at the fellow's face, trying hard to see the truth behind his jesting. So the man they knew only as Mr. X, with the name of 'Jim Phelps' and wearing a skin-mask in Jim's likeness, was an Orientalian agent. Poor old Barney! He'd have been taken care of and the briefcase holding the tritium device would be on its way to the White House, where he and Rollin were prisoners of the Federal Security Forces. Surely a peculiar situation!

Sitting back under the gun of a guard, he began to think the thing out. The man with the face-mask of Jim Phelps would appear at the South Gate *without the mask*, in his real identity as the supposed I.M.F. agent, would be admitted in all innocence, as he would have the electronic identity card. He began to sweat a little and looked at Rollin. Hand's dark, saturnine face was immobile as always, but the same bitter thoughts would be in his mind.

Even so, as prisoners in the little guard-house they did have a point of vantage, and when the car drove out of the traffic stream on Pennsylvania Avenue and he saw the man with a brief-case climb out, he realised that there was a wild card in the game. This fellow was a total stranger.

While the man was having his I.D. card checked through the electronic checker, Jim touched Rollin lightly on the foot. "Up to us now, Rollin," he muttered.

"There's the briefcase. And they're letting it in."

Rollin moved spasmodically, and the guard cocked his gun.

"That man," grunted Hand, "that fellow in the security uniform with that case – you've got to stop him. He's got a bomb—" Then he dried up, realising that this was a secret even from these guards.

"Quit that malarkey," growled the guard. "Hey, sarge, that guy okay?"

"Sure," called the Sergeant. "One of us, seconded as aide to one of the Joint Chiefs. Got a case filled with papers for his boss."

"This guy says somethin' about a bomb," the guard said, waving his gun towards the two captives.

"*Bomb!*" jerked the sergeant, and he turned back towards the newcomer.

But he was too late. The man was sneaking into the shrubbery when a phantom leaped from another car at the gate and hurtled past the sergeant and the other guards; he brought the fugitive down with a football tackle.

The guards piled on top of the pair, and the stranger lay on the ground, knocked out.

A twin of Jim Phelps got up, grasping the briefcase. "I'll take this, sergeant," he said crisply, and Jim Phelps recognised Barney's voice. With a sigh of relief, he laughed, and Rollin Hand gave a sardonic, wintry chuckle as he saw Cinnamon in front of the small crowd that had gathered outside the South Gate.

"Keep out, lady," howled the sergeant, as Cinnamon strolled in. "Ain't we got enough trouble?"

Cinnamon tossed her red hair and laughed. "You'll need me to sort out all this double and treble identity." She turned to the two twins of Jim Phelps. "Well, this mission didn't turn out all that impossible, Jim, did it?" she remarked. And she was speaking to the real Jim Phelps this time.

MISSION: IMPOSSIBLE

The Weathermen Plot

FROM SOMEWHERE IN GERMANIA A WEATHER STATION WAS OPERATING WITH DEVASTATING RESULTS FOR VAST AGRICULTURAL AREAS IN OTHER COUNTRIES. CROPS WERE BEING RUINED, TOWNS AND VILLAGES SEVERELY DAMAGED AND PEOPLE BEING KILLED BY TERRIFIC ARTIFICIAL STORMS PRODUCED BY THE GERMANIAN WEATHERMEN.

JIM PHELPS' ASSIGNMENT WAS DIRECT. PLANT A HOMING DEVICE FOR NUCLEAR MISSILES IN THE WEATHERMEN'S BASE

THE BASE MUST BE DESTROYED AT ALL COSTS OR WE FACE ECONOMIC RUIN!

THIS WATCH CARRIES A MICRO SIGNAL BEAMER. PLANT YOUR HOMING DEVICE, THEN WHEN YOU BEAM US WE'LL DESPATCH NUCLEAR MISSILES WHICH WILL HOME ON THE HOMING DEVICE YOU HAD BETTER BE CLEAR OF THAT BASE WITHIN FIFTEEN MINUTES OF YOUR SENDING THE SIGNAL.

UNDERSTOOD!

JIM DECIDED TO TAKE WILLIE AND BARNEY ON THE ASSIGNMENT.

WILLIE WILL BE CONTACT MAN. HE'LL TIP YOU OFF WHERE AND WHEN.

...AND I'LL BE READY WITH A CAR TO MOVE IN AND PICK YOU UP IMMEDIATELY.

A FEW DAYS LATER IN NONBON, THE GERMANIAN CAPITAL....

OUR INFORMATION WAS EXCELLENT. THAT TRUCK ACROSS THE STREET IS BEING LOADED FOR THE WEATHER BASE. I'M ON MY WAY!

SOON JIM WAS JOLTING ALONG ON HIS PRECARIOUS RIDE..

THE TRUCK WAS PASSED THROUGH THE SECRET GERMANIAN COMPLEX.

PHEW! I CAN'T HOLD ON MUCH LONGER.

ONCE INSIDE THE AREA, JIM JUMPED CLEAR.

JIM SWITCHED ON THE SIGNAL BEAMER IMMEDIATELY...

I'M CUTTING MY SAFETY MARGIN BUT I DON'T WANT TO RISK THE GERMANIANS LOCATING THE HOMING DEVICE AND IMMOBIL-ISING IT

THE SIGNAL WAS RECEIVED AT JIM'S HOME BASE AND...

OPERATION WEATHERMEN SIGNAL RECEIVED. MISSILE STRIKE AWAY

IMMEDIATELY THE DEADLY MISSILES WERE DESPATCHED...

BUT THE SIGNAL WAS ALSO PICKED UP AT THE GERMANIAN BASE ...

SEARCH THE AREA IMMEDIATELY!

THERE'S AN UNACCOUNT-ABLE DEVICE SOMEWHERE IN THE MAIN AREA!

MEANWHILE ...

THE ALARM'S BEEN GIVEN, LET'S HOPE THE DEVICE ISN'T FOUND BEFORE THE MISSILES ARRIVE.

THEN...

QUICK! THAT MAN SEEMS IN A BIG HURRY. GRAB HIM!

HEY, YOU! STOP!

MY TIME'S RUNNING OUT.

MEANWHILE NOT FAR AWAY...

TIME TO MAKE MY MOVE

IF THE TIMING IS OUT I'LL GET TO THE BASE IN TIME TO BE BLOWN TO BITS.

MEANWHILE, JIM IS IN REAL TROUBLE

RIGHT! DON'T TREAT HIM GENTLY

GET HIM OUTSIDE AND PUT HIM UP AGAINST A WALL!

AT THAT MOMENT BARNEY STORMED IN, SMASHING THROUGH THE PERIMETER GATE...

JIM WAS QUICK TO TAKE ADVANTAGE OF THE CONFUSION...

HE SEIZED A WEAPON AND BACKED OFF TOWARD BARNEY'S CAR...

PHEW! NOT MUCH TIME LEFT.

SECONDS LATER JIM MADE A DASH FOR IT...

STEP ON IT, BARNEY! ONLY MINUTES OFF THE BIG BANG!

BARNEY AND JIM SPED AWAY TO SAFETY. MINUTES LATER THE GERMANIAN BASE WAS BLOWN TO ETERNITY ..

THE JACKBOOT KICKS

"It's a tough one, Jim."
The voice from the tiny cassette tape-recorder was measured and unemotional. It was the same male voice that always gave Jim Phelps the details of assignments offered to his team of undercover agents.

Jim was at the wheel of a sleek Ford Thunderbird. He had switched to this car from his own as part of the pre-arranged routine for avoiding any possible shadowing by rival agents. The tape-recorder had been waiting on the passenger seat, ready to be switched on.

"Understand, Jim? If you and your colleagues decide to take on the job, you're on your own. If anything goes wrong, there can be no question of help from us ... Now, here are the details – and you'll find an envelope beside you with photographs of some of the people concerned. They're all connected with an outfit called Jackboot Publications. . . ."

The cool voice spoke on as Jim made the turn at 42nd Street, and eased over into the southbound lane. He looked relaxed, but his highly-trained mind was intensely busy memorising every word from the midget tape.

His big hands lay easily on the steering wheel. His eyes flicked occasionally to the rear-view mirror. Something about a car behind him began to nag faintly. It was a dark, sleek Mercedes-Benz, with a girl at the wheel.

". . . Obviously, Jackboot Publications is a mere cover for something else. And if our information is correct, that 'something' is a lethal threat to public authority. . . ."

The recorded message was coming to an end. Jim let his mind ease into low gear as he gave the big car the gas and let it ride into top gear. Almost subconsciously he had turned east onto Tennant Boulevarde, leaving the mainstream of traffic behind.

His eyes sought the rear-view mirror again. The Mercedes-Benz was still there. Jim suddenly lost interest in the recorded voice at his side. Years of training had developed a razor-sharp sense of danger.

The Mercedes was moving up fast to overtake. Jim held his speed and watched. Now his knuckles were white round the wheel.

But there was nothing to warn him of the faint wisp of smoke that curled over his shoulder from behind the driving-seat. Its acrid smell and bitter taste set off full-scale alarm bells inside his brain.

He shook his head, thumbed the button that lowered the power-windows, and gulped the chill air-stream ... but it was too late.

As he felt the first wave of nausea and blackness, Jim slewed the car off the road and ground to a halt. His head sagged on the wheel, and from a far distance he heard the calm voice on tape saying: "That's all, Jim. This tape will self-destruct in ten seconds. Good luck."

The Mercedes-Benz slid to a halt behind the agent's car. The girl dived from behind the wheel with a flash of long, elegant legs. As she ran for the Thunderbird, a thin voice lisped in her ears: "Get the tape! Get the tape!"

But even as the girl reached a gloved hand through the open window of the car to snatch the tape-recorder, it emitted a tiny hiss, and a wisp of acrid smoke curled upward from it.

She slammed the side panel petulantly in her annoyance. From the tiny speaker hidden in her ear-rings the lisping voice queried: "Well? Did you get it, Dilawn?"

"No, Carl!" She spat the words elegantly from between tight lips.

"Too bad.... Bring him in, then." The voice spoke briefly, then crackled into silence.

Barney smoothed out the map he had unfolded on the table. He looked around at the grim faces

56

of his fellow-agents – Rollin Hand, the expert in disguises, Willy the strong man, and beautiful Cinnamon, who posed as a fashion model.

They had gathered at the headquarters of Impossible Missions Force as soon as they heard of the capture of their leader.

"We've got to work fast," said Barney quietly. "They've taken Jim to the Jackboot building down town – here!" He stabbed at the map with a forefinger. The others bent close to look.

Barney's voice went on unemotionally: "They missed the message on the tape, so they aim to work on Jim until he snaps – and talks."

"Jim will never do that!" said Cinnamon, her eyes flashing.

"We all know that – if they use conventional methods," agreed Barney. "But they're flying someone special in from Detroit to do the job. . . . Here's his picture."

They all stared at the thin, sallow face in the photograph that Barney had tossed before them. Cinnamon could not repress a shudder at the sight of the thin, cruel lips and the blazing eyes. "Who is he?" she whispered.

"Amalfi. An expert in hypnotism," said Barney. He turned towards Rollin Hand. "Can you make-up like Amalfi in a hurry?" he wanted to know.

Rollin picked up the picture and studied it intently. "What about the voice?" he asked.

Barney took a cassette tape from his pocket. "Our Detroit agent taped Amalfi as he was giving a performance in a night club."

Rollin took the tape and nodded. "I'll be ready in an hour," he promised.

"Make that half an hour. The plane from Detroit lands in thirty-five minutes. Willy and I will be there to see that Amalfi is put in the bag, while you take his place walking into the airport terminal building. Get going, Rollin! I'll fill you in on what to do as we ride out to the airport," said Barney.

As the disguise expert hurried from the room, Cinnamon said: "What about me, Barney? I'm not being left out of this, am I?"

"Not on your life," replied the other, with a tight grin. "You've already been booked to pose for some fashion pictures for one of Jackboot's flashier publications."

Cinnamon's eyes lit up. "Good.

And when I'm in – what's the pitch?"

"Stay beautiful!" urged Barney. "Keep 'em busy till zero hour – and then raise a little hell."

He handed the girl a small gold compact. "Handle it gently," he warned. "Use it at three-five exactly. Then get up on the roof." He turned to where the big-shouldered Willy had been patiently waiting for his orders. "You'll be on the roof by that time, Willy. As soon as Cinnamon shows, plant this fire-cracker – and the two of you get the hell out of there! Okay?"

Willy took the small leather case that Barney handed to him. "Leave it to me," he nodded.

"Then take a good look at this map of the Jackboot building, and let's go over the plan," said Barney. "This is one mission that *has* to succeed!"

Jim Phelps felt the salty taste of blood in his mouth. His head reeled from the vicious blow that he had just received. His head lolled on his chest, and he leaned against the ropes that bound him to a surgery-type chair in the middle of the cold, echoing room.

"You will talk, Mr. Agent. Never fear – you will tell us all we want to know," said a lisping voice.

Through a haze of pain, Jim looked up at the white-faced little man bending over him. Behind the man loomed the bulky figures of the two muscle-men who had been working him over.

"Like I said before, I've got nothing to tell you," said Jim thickly. He braced himself for another flurry of blows – but they never came. There was a buzz of a telephone, and Carl, the man with the lisp, waved his henchmen away impatiently.

"You apes have failed!" he lisped harshly. "Now we'll try a little finesse." He walked to where

58

the telephone hung on the wall. "Yes?" he said into the mouth-piece. "All right. Send him in here at once."

A moment later the door opened and two more thugs came into the empty room with a rather sinister-looking figure, who flung aside his cloak with a theatrical gesture.

"You are Amalfi?" lisped Carl.

Rollin took no notice of his question. He was mincing about the room, snapping his fingers and listening intently. "No, no, the acoustics are all wrong!" he rasped, turning on the little man. "Get your men to bring in the rubber mats I've brought. I was afraid of something like this. You people have no idea!"

Carl's eyes narrowed dangerously. "Now look here, Amalfi—" he began.

"No, *you* listen to me!" snarled Rollin, tapping the other on the chest. "You want this man to talk, don't you? I can make him tell you everything. But it's got to be done *my* way."

Carl choked back his wrath. "Bring the stuff in!" he lisped to his muscle-men.

For the next ten minutes, Rollin had the thugs spreading the thick rubber mats on the floor around the chair in which Jim was strapped.

Jim fought to control the fear that grew unbidden within him as he watched the preparations.

Amalfi was setting up an ominous array of gadgets, with which he was to try and probe the mind of his 'patient'. The most terrifying of these 'torture' implements was a switchboard that emitted a low-pitched drone, and flashed a series of brilliant lights in all directions. From this board, Amalfi led a flex to where Jim was sitting. He forced a metal clamp onto his victim's head, and wired the flex to terminals.

"Now, I'm all ready," declared Amalfi, turning to the watching men. "You will kindly leave me to my work. Anything he says will be tape-recorded."

Carl frowned. "You think I'm going to leave you alone with him? Oh, no. He's much too valuable for that," he lisped.

It looked as though the hypnotist was about to yell back. But with a mighty effort he controlled himself and waved his watchers into a corner. "Keep away from me, then," he warned. "Stay there and keep quiet. One sound could ruin everything. . . . Now, turn out those lights."

Carl hesitated at this command. Then he yielded, and waved his hand. One of the thugs turned the switch, and the room was plunged into darkness. A moment later the 'mind-probe' machine began to howl on a higher note, and the blinding lights began to flash. Amalfi bent over his victim. . . .

Jim's heart tightened a little, and then a flood of relief swept over him as he recognised Rollin's voice in his ear: "Make it look good, Jim. Scream; then start talking. We've got to keep these goons entertained until Barney bores up through this floor. He's

operating from the cable tunnel below the building!"

Carl and his henchmen saw the figure in the chair begin to writhe in agony. Suddenly, an unnatural howl of terror left his lips: "Aa-aah! Don't! Stop . . ! Please!"

The air in the dank blackness of the cable-tunnel was stale and almost overpowering. In spite of the chillness, Barney had to pause in his work to brush away the perspiration running down his face.

He glanced at his watch. The luminous hands told him that he had exactly twenty-three minutes to Zero Hour. Grimly, he tightened his aching hands around the hypersonic cutter, and went to work on the tunnel he was boring upwards. By means of ultra-high frequency sound waves, his amazing tool could slice through the toughest material in double-quick time. . . . But double-quick was hardly enough now. Barney knew that his chances of getting through to the basement cell by Zero Hour were mighty slim. . . .

He thumbed the switch and the high-pitched snarl rose to an ear-splitting pitch. Barney heard it faintly through his ear plugs, and saw the mist of pulverised concrete drifting onto his goggles. . . .

Cinnamon put on her Mona Lisa smile as the long-haired young man bent over his camera. "Okay, darling! That's a great pose! Hold it!" he exclaimed.

The camera whirred again. It had been whirring steadily for the past half-hour. Cinnamon had posed in a variety of stylish clothes. But she had been busy in another direction, too. For the studio in which she was working had a window that allowed her glimpses of what was going on in an adjoining room. At a casual glance it seemed as though the white-coated men and women busy at desks and benches were engaged in routine tasks of parcelling books for despatch. But

Cinnamon's trained eye soon spotted more sinister undertones to the activities.

"Now, if he's not inserting microdot film on those pages, I miss my bet!" she told herself, as she watched one of the men bending over the pages of the book, and working with tweezers under a magnifying glass.

A new change of clothes, and a different pose ten minutes later, allowed her another interesting glimpse. This time she saw pages of books being impregnated with a chemical spray.

A glance at her watch told Cinnamon that there were nine minutes left to Zero Hour. "Time I was getting ready to use my little gadget for creating the diversion," she told herself, fingering the small gold compact in her pocket.

At that moment a girl came into the studio. She was good-looking, but rather hard-faced, elegantly dressed and coiffeured.

"Hi, Miss Dilawn!" greeted the photographer over his shoulder.

Cinnamon found the other girl's eyes examining her with a penetrating stare. She pretended not to notice, but her sharp ears caught the other's low voice as she asked the photographer: "Who's the model? Haven't seen her before."

The young man answered her.

Dilawn frowned. "Strange . . . she reminds me of someone."

There was something in the way that the girl turned and went out quickly from the studio that sounded a note of warning inside Cinnamon's pretty head. "Could be she's checking on me," she thought.

She went on posing for shots, looking very relaxed, but feeling horribly tense as the seconds ticked by to Zero Hour. . . .

With seventy seconds to go, Dilawn reappeared. Cinnamon could see by her face that her theory had been correct.

"We've been neatly fooled, Charles," purred Dilawn to the photographer. "This isn't a model! She's an agent like the one we're working on in the basement. . . . Get her down off that stand, and lock her up."

Cinnamon didn't need to check her watch to know that Zero

Hour had arrived. She ducked under the photographer's grappling arms, and disposed of him with a neat kick. Then she tossed her compact across the room, and dived to the floor.

BOOM! The explosion seemed to rock the whole Jackboot building. As dust and powdered glass rained down around her, Cinnamon heard the alarm bells begin. . . .

Rollin and Jim heard them, too. The basement room was still in darkness, except for the flashing lights of the amazing 'information extractor'. Jim was hoarse from yelling in pretended pain, and gabbling out 'secrets' for the benefit of the Jackboot listeners.

But now the alarm bells put an end to their charade. Rollin heard Carl yell: "Switch on those lights! Keep your guns ready!"

At the same moment the floor beneath the mat began to tremble. Rollin turned the howl from his machine to full volume. "Let's go, Jim!" he yelled into his victim's ear. With one hand he snapped the bonds that secured Jim to the chair. With the other he tossed a small pellet in the direction of Carl and his henchmen.

The pellet broke at their feet, sending up a cloud of choking fumes. Coughing and gasping, the gunmen staggered back.

Jim and Rollin were already tearing aside the mat. Below, they found the hole that Barney had just cut through from the cable-tunnel. In another moment the two men had dropped from sight. . . .

"Well, it's great to have you back, Jim," said Barney.

He was expressing the feelings of all the Mission Impossible team as they relaxed in easy chairs at headquarters an hour later.

"I'm sure glad you were able to spring me," smiled Jim. "Thanks."

Rollin was still pulling the plastic make-up mask from his face. He glanced over his shoulder. "The only thing I don't understand is how you managed to get out safely after that girl discovered who you were, Cinnamon."

She shrugged slim shoulders. "It was easier than I expected," she said. "I found the bomb had blasted a hole in the wall of the office I'd been so interested in. So I just slipped in, picked up a pile of books and walked upstairs to the roof, carrying them in front of my face and pretending to be a busy office worker . . . Willy was waiting for me on the roof – and we used his high-wire gadget to get clear."

Jim rose to his feet and crossed to where Willy was examining the books piled on the table. "Interesting, eh?" he said. "It was a brilliant idea to get hold of these books. The way Jackboot fixed them up, they're pretty lethal weapons. And almost every important man in world government was on Jackboot's mailing list! Thank heavens we blew their little plot sky high!"

IMPOSSIBLE PEOPLE

Jim Phelps and his 'impossible' team often have to disguise themselves with skin masks and various other forms of concealment, and pretend to be someone else in order to succeed in their mission. But there have always been impostors who, for personal gain, revenge, or merely for the excitement of hoaxing the public, have successfully impersonated people far removed from their own personal lives.

THE MAIDSERVANT PRINCESS

Such a one was a certain Mary Baker, once employed as a servant in a Bath household, who one day arrived in a Gloucestershire village, speaking a strange language and calling herself Princess Caraboo.

She completely hoodwinked everyone of importance in Almondsbury in that April of 1817, including the local gentry, who were fascinated by the fact that the princess ate only fruit, refused to sleep in a bed, and always carried a quiver full of arrows, and a bow.

She was treated just like visiting royalty and people bowed and kissed her hand when they came to see her, but a newspaper article was to prove Princess Caraboo's downfall.

Reading of this Eastern princess, the keeper of a lodging house at Bath was struck by the resemblance of the princess to a servant who had been a great source of amusement to the household on account of the fanciful stories she told about herself.

But, even though she was now unmasked, Mary's luck still held, for she was offered a new life in America, and set sail as an immigrant to the New World.

Despite what had already happened, Mary was still eager for adventure, and once again she risked the danger of exposure as an impostor when, wishing to see the great Napoleon on St. Helena, Mary secretly left the ship and by some miraculous means succeeded in meeting 'The Little General'.

Napoleon was greatly impressed by Princess Caraboo and actually told his English gaoler that he would have liked to have married the princess had he not been married already!

GRIN, THE CANNIBAL CHIEF

What eventually happened to Mary Baker is shrouded in mystery, but we do know that Grin, the cannibal chief, had to sell matches in the streets of London when an enterprising newspaper finally revealed that Louis de Rougemont, self-styled chief of an aborigine tribe of cannibals, was none other than a wandering Swiss workman who had once had a series of humble jobs in Australia.

But before being finally unmasked Grin had persuaded many influential people that he was a French nobleman who had had the misfortune to have been shipwrecked off the Australian coast and had lived for many years with the aborigines, who finally made him their leader.

In a leading geographical magazine Grin wrote a detailed account of his adventures,

THE CAPTAIN OF KOEPENICK

But a story with a happier ending is that of the 'Captain of Koepenick', who in reality was a humble shoemaker named Voigt. This man, contemptuous of the manner in which a uniform impressed the Germans in the early twentieth century, and eager to repay a slight on the part of the local mayor, resolved to show how easily anyone could play the part of a person of importance, provided he had the right clothes.

Dressed as a Prussian officer, he ordered a troop of soldiers to accompany him to the mayor of Koepenick's official offices. He then placed the mayor under arrest while he insisted that the town treasurer gave him all the town's money.

Although Voigt was later caught and imprisoned for his audacious crime, the whole world was amused by his boldness, and when he was released from prison William Voigt became an actor, amusing audiences as the bold 'Captain of Koepenick', who had truly proved that 'fine feathers make a fine bird'.

THE LADY GENERAL

The reason why these impostors posed as someone else is clear; they all wanted to make their lives a little more exciting. But James Barry carried the reason for *her* hidden identity with her to the grave . . . Nobody ever knew the reason why this girl, grandchild of an earl, never told anyone her real name, and carved out a career for herself as a naval officer, without anyone ever realising that the young surgeon, quick-tempered and easily offended, was a woman.

Perhaps her family had wanted a boy, or perhaps she herself wished she had been born a male; but whatever the reason, it seems amazing that aboard ship nobody discovered that Surgeon Barry, who had trained at a famous London teaching hospital, was of the female sex.

And Captain Barry seemed to do everything to make the other naval officers notice him. He fought a duel, walked about with a huge dog and a great, coloured servant at his heels, and was continually in conflict with senior officers. Yet, despite all this, his secret remained undiscovered!

The naval surgeon made many influential friends because, despite his brusque manner, he was a clever and skilful doctor, and by the time he retired he had risen to the rank of general.

It was only on his death, in 1865, that it was discovered that the general was, in fact, a lady!

which grew wilder and wilder as the story progressed, and finally aroused the suspicions of the *Daily Chronicle* as to its authenticity.

Relentlessly the newspaper continued to make enquiries, probing remorselessly into the details which Grin — or Monsieur de Rougemont, as he preferred to be known — had so foolishly supplied. These had included his fight with a tomahawk against an alligator, his incredible journey by turtle to the island from the shipwreck, and the description of wombats that flew!

When finally confronted with undisputed evidence of his trickery, the bogus chief admitted that he had gathered all the material for his articles from the British Museum. Although he was an impostor, one must admit to a grudging admiration for someone who would go to so much trouble to perfect his hoax.

"Close to home this time," said Jim Phelps casually, as he held the flaming reel of tape over the destructor chute. "Right on our doorstep, as a matter of fact; East 30th Street, the Segatto Building."

Lifting the phone he dialled a number, spoke one word – "Accepted" – then replaced the receiver.

Cinnamon was looking out of the window, down at the passing traffic. Barney was looking into space, while Willy and Rollin Hand were sitting, apparently thinking of nothing at all.

An observer would never have known that any of the four were paying any attention to their leader but, when he didn't immediately go on, four pairs of eyebrows were raised.

"Playing nursemaid is the job," grinned Jim. "A penthouse on top of the Segatto Building holds two human beings. Just at the moment those two human beings are maybe the most valuable people in the world to our Government."

"Hostages?" asked Barney curiously. Jim laughed.

"Wake up, Barney," he said. "That's not the way we work. Our mission is to prevent them from *becoming* hostages. They are the wife and child of the largest industrialist in Frankelia in Europe. Our Government wants a base there and this man, now in

MAFIA MAYDAY

Washington conferring with the Secretary of State, is the man who can influence his Government to do what our boys want."

"Who's the opposition, Jim?" asked Rollin Hand, absent-mindedly.

Jim Phelps did not reply directly, but his next words told them the answer. "This guy – multi-millionaire industrialist, oil tycoon, and heavy goods vehicle manufacturer – has one strike against him in our estimation. That's why the State Department

was all steamed up when he brought his family with him, secretly. They claim he should have left them behind in his own country, suitably guarded. But Mike Gobbo, that's his name, wouldn't dare do that at the moment. They're guarded well *outside* the flat, but Gobbo's up against something which in its time has overthrown governments, started wars, and caused financial panics in countries as big as ours."

Rollin Hand nodded, as if

agreeing with something he'd been thinking.

"The Mafia?" he said casually, and Jim nodded.

"Gobbo was once a member, when he lived as a youth in Sicily. Then he got out, came to this country and made a fortune. He went back to Frankelia and, strangely enough, they let him alone. He probably was black-mailed into giving them large sums of money; we don't know that. In fact, no one outside the Mafia knew of his early connection until our Central Intelligence Agency dug up the fact, quite by chance. By then it was too late for our side. They'd already started dickering with him, and his family were in residence in the Segatto penthouse, which he owns."

"He'll have his own guards," said Cinnamon. "He'll have the F.B.I., the C.I.A. and the ordinary cops. Where do *we* come in?"

"The essence of the job, Cinnamon," Jim said briskly, "is that the Mafia have sworn to kidnap the woman and the child, then kill them if Gobbo throws his lot in with us. And they can do that sort of thing, we all know. It's our job to stop 'em from doing it and, if possible, spirit the two away to what we think is a safer place. The reason we got the mission is the fact that it's the Mafia who are on the job, and the fact that Gobbo was once a member must not, repeat not, become known to the general public. He's sent out a 'Mayday' call and we're behind the eight-ball. So now we start planning."

"Mrs. Gobbo is going to acquire another maid, Jim, I should figure," smiled Cinnamon.

Jim laughed. "You're way ahead of me, Cinnamon, but as usual you're on the ball. You'll be a governess for Mike's child. Willy, you're on the elevator. That should be simple enough to arrange, as the lift to the penthouse is private."

"That leaves the garbage cans for me," said Barney, with a disgusted twist of his lips. "I always seem to get the dirty jobs."

"It was your own idea, Barney," chuckled Jim. "You seem to have cast yourself in that role. But you're good with lifts too, aren't you? Fascinating things, elevators. I've known you to almost make them eat out of your hand. Well now, you people seem to be planning ahead of schedule. I guess that, working as a team as we do, that comes natural. Only Rollin and myself are left."

"I suppose we'll be the strong-arm squad," said Rollin, smiling bleakly. "Sitting in the corners of the sitting-room with guns in shoulder-holsters. How long is the vigil to be?"

"Maybe up to a week," said Jim thoughtfully. "The talking and the negotiating will take that long. One or two of us just may have to take the family back to Frankelia when it's over."

The transfer of Cinnamon to the penthouse staff was easy enough for Jim Phelps to organise between himself and the State Department.

Willy's insertion into the elevator staff was more tricky. The three elevator men on the private

shaft proved to be staunch fellows, immune to bribery, and Willy had to resort to primitive methods. Barney carried away the unconscious elevator man in the cab of his garbage truck, and Willy donned the uniform, blandly informing the other two shift men that he was their co-worker's cousin, standing in for the other, who was suffering from some mysterious illness.

Barney came back, and he and Willy went over the elevator system, floor by floor, cable by cable and wheel by wheel. An elaborate knowledge of the mechanism might be vital in the days to come.

Mrs. Mike Gobbo was a simple Frankelian peasant woman, bewildered with the new world into which her husband's wealth and power had moved her. The child, Carmelita, eight years of age, was a fragile little olive-skinned girl, and Cinnamon found her heart going out to these two, pawns in this game of international intrigue.

She settled in quickly, and the reason for her presence was never mentioned. Mrs. Gobbo was one of those people who accept whatever comes along. But Cinnamon was frankly disturbed when there was no sign of Jim and Rollin. At the end of her first day she mentioned this to Willy, on duty on the private lift.

"That's all right," Willy told her. "Barney received word; slight change of plan. Seems this threatened snatch hasn't got any one set scheme. These Mafia boys are opportunists; they play the game step by step, and improvise. That way they find it better to deal with sudden emergencies."

"They've been taking leaves out of our book," said Cinnamon dryly. "But one side or the other must have an edge some time. Who has it right now?"

"It's our turn at the ace, Cinnamon," grinned Barney, coming from the kitchen with a can of garbage on his shoulder. "Jim and Rollin have found out something that means it's best for them not to be here. The snatch was timed for three in the morning, tomorrow. That's been brought forward. Expect callers round one o'clock. Willy will keep the lift up at the top floor and I'll be around."

Cinnamon was always calm and at one o'clock next morning, as serene as ever, she sat in the kitchen, trying not to look at the hands of the clock, which jerked slowly up towards the hour.

Dead on time, she heard the thrashing of a helicopter's vanes, and she got to her feet. Willy was at the open door of his elevator, and Barney was inside. They joined her in the kitchen and listened together.

"They're both asleep in the big bedroom," Cinnamon said. "That's a 'copter. Is it the Mafia, or could it be Jim and Rollin?"

Both shrugged. "According to Jim," Barney said, "we play the cards as they are dealt. If the Mafia's calling, we cope. Right?"

"Right," said Willy impassively. "Stay in the kitchen, Cinnamon."

"Think again, Willy," the girl retorted. "I'm in this too, remember."

The 'copter's motors sounded like harsh thunder as it hovered over the flat roof surrounding the penthouse. As it landed they could hear the thud, even through the brick, concrete and steel of the roof. Barney and Willy, with guns drawn, had hidden behind easy chairs.

On the settee, Cinnamon smoked a cigarette, thoughtfully, feeling like the goat staked out as bait for the tiger. She felt the round muzzle of a pistol in the back of her neck, but she did not turn round.

"Just keep nice and still and quiet, sister," said a foreign voice. "We've got a job to do and we ain't wanting to hurt you. Where's the bedrooms?"

"Lay off the dame, Angelo," came another voice. "We know where they are. Just hold her there and I'll do the rest. We don't want

no noise and . . ."

"But we do," said Barney harshly, and he and Willy rose like ghosts from behind their chairs.

Willy flew at the one who was threatening Cinnamon, and the butt of his gun came down hard on the fellow's elbow. With a crisp oath he turned, and Willy drove a balled fist into his stomach, hard.

Barney was tearing into the other, a short, fat, dark-faced Frankelian. The bullet from his gun whistled through Barney's hair, and then he was at the man's throat. They struggled fiercely, and then Barney had him down and was squatting on his chest.

All three were watching when the two men regained consciousness. To their surprise the 'copter had gone away and all was silent out on the roof.

When the pair came back to life Barney was watching them curiously. Their attitude was very far from being that of two killer-

thugs thwarted in their designs. Rather they sat up and felt their bumps and grinned all round.

"You got it all wrong, fellas and lady," said the fat one. "We ain't crooks. We're guards, sent to look after the two chicks here. Word's got round that the Mafia are out to kidnap 'em. Can you lick that?"

"Most extraordinary," agreed Willy gravely.

"Handy way of dropping in, by helicopter," said Barney sarcastically.

"Oh, we know you Mafia guys are slippery," said Angelo. "Giuseppe and me, we figured we'd play it smart. Now, we knew that the elevator was going to be fixed, so we came in at the top. You guys seem to have the jump on us. Well, you can't win 'em all."

Willy got up and went out. A moment later he came back.

"Lift's stuck down on the ninth," he said solemnly. "Cinnamon, you keep a gun on these two birds while Barney and me go down and fix it."

"You won't get away with this, you know," bluffed Angelo. "There's plenty of cops in the street outside."

Barney eyed them stonily. He didn't believe for one moment that these rats were under the impression that their captors were Mafia members. What had gone wrong? He looked at Cinnamon and gestured towards the bedroom.

She came back in a moment, her eyes stricken, but her face as calm as ever.

Sitting down, she whispered into Barney's ear: "Both gone, and bed's mussed up. Open windows. 'Copter crew must have snatched them while we were fighting these apes."

Barney relaxed his breathing, but kept his face straight. They

had failed, then. Well, Jim and Rollin were abroad, and he had known that in this game many of the cards were wild. But this looked pretty bad; the 'copter gone and the woman and the child. In a big country they could be anywhere. Passing the gun silently to Cinnamon, he got up and went out.

Peering down the shaft, he saw Willy disappearing through the roof trap into the stalled elevator car and he looked up at the head mechanism of the installation. Reaching out for the swaying cables, he climbed up them.

It was a simple blockage, and he had it right inside five minutes. But he could do nothing while Willy was down there. He couldn't activate the machinery from the top; that was up to Willy, down in the car. How to reach him in time? He went back inside, thinking hard.

No sooner had he rejoined the girl than they heard the whirring of the elevator, and then in burst Willy, followed by two white-coated men.

Shaking his head, Barney saw Jim and Rollin. "Tell me what goes on, Jim?" he said blankly.

"Long story, Barney," rapped

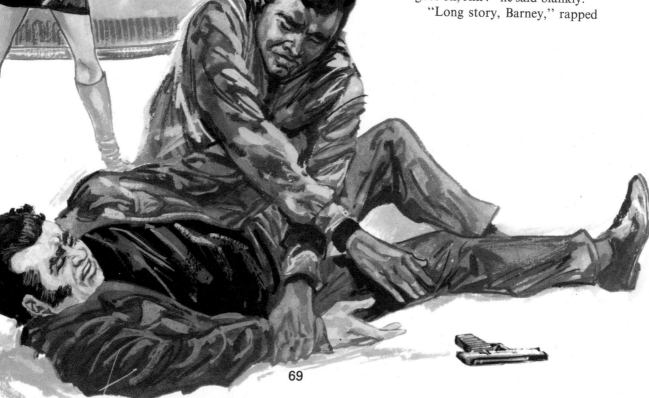

Jim. "Can't tell it all right now. No time. We take these two crumbs with us. Ambulance below, with escort. We're due at Idlewild in the half-hour. Take us all our time to make it."

It was obvious that the two Mafia thugs were dumbfounded by the appearance of the two I.M.F. men. They started to protest and swear, but Jim cold-bloodedly chopped them each behind an ear, and then he and Rollin expertly laced them into the stretchers they had brought, and they all went down.

A motorcycle police escort awaited them and, with sirens howling, they cut through the traffic. Barney, Willy and Cinnamon waited to hear the story.

Rollin, dark-faced and saturnine as always, was actually the first to speak. Jim, driving, was much too engrossed.

"We couldn't get in touch and, anyway, there had to be some of us on the spot. The fact is, we found out very late that the Mafia weren't planning to kidnap Mrs. Gobbo and the girl. That threat was just a blind to keep us off the real plan: that was to snatch Gobbo himself. They'd have cut his throat, of course. They usually follow that delightful plan when they catch up with a former member who's dropped out. Gobbo's safe now, in a jet waiting at Idlewild."

"What about the woman and the child?" asked Cinnamon, anxiously.

"Oh, that 'copter was crewed, along with Angelo and Giuseppe back there, by two of our boys passing off as gangsters. Mrs. Gobbo and the girl will be at the airport right now, joining father. The talks with the State Department are all over and everything has been agreed. Gobbo's going to arrange it with his government. The Mafia drew all low cards this time, gang."

SPY A JOKE!

Well MZ 2½, I've just received another anonymous letter. . . .
Oh, yes, sir. Who is it from this time?

Wow, M7, I thought mine were white until now!

Just what is that supposed to be, Agent Smith, an identikit, or the latest 'painting by numbers'?

JK to control. I've captured the quarry sir. Yes, he's with me right now. . .

THE SEVENTH SANTA CLAUS

Jim Phelps and Barney watched the line of men in the yard behind the large agency building. Barney's face broke into a broad grin.

"They handed us a hot one this time, Jim," he said. "Seventeen of these guys, and all as much alike as peas in a pod. We have to move fast at this point, Jim. These fellows will all be in seventeen big department stores by this afternoon."

The seventeen men lined up were all in red woollen gowns with hoods over their white hair. All of them had long white beards and all of them carried sacks which were, at the moment, empty. The two men from the employment agency were walking up and down in front of them scrutinising their dress and make-up. To the two men from the Impossible Missions Force they all looked exactly alike, allowing for slight differences in height and bulk.

"We have one clue, Barney," murmured Jim, and under cover of his hand he checked again with the photo that was shielded in his palm. "A tiny wart on the left of his nose, Barney. Take a quick look; we've not much time left."

"Warts now, is it?" said Barney and his quick eye went along the line. "I spy two warted Santas. One on the right of the nose and . . . left, you said. That's our man, Jim. Tenth from this end. We nab him now, eh?"

"No, repeat no," chuckled Jim. "The exchange hasn't been made. This guy is just a small cell in the Oringian spy network. We're after the Big One. This man is supposed by C.I.A. to have the package the Big Boy will pick up from him. But we don't know when, and we've only the haziest idea of what will be in the package. Just as well we don't know, either. Between our boys and the Oringians there's so little to choose in weapons that, if Oringia wants it so badly as to go through all this comic rigmarole to get it moving, it must be something pretty ghastly and well wrapped up. So, we don't look. Now, where's Rollin?"

Rollin Hand came out of the small door with the director of the employment agency. He passed close to Jim and Barney, who stood at the front of the small crowd which had come to laugh at this parade of Santas.

As Rollin came opposite them, Jim murmured to him, "Round the rear, Rollin. Seventh from the far end."

Jim grinned at Barney as they watched Rollin and the director go along the row and round to the back. They saw him pat the shoulders of one or two of the

72

men to see that their uniforms fitted well, and saw him halt for a second at the seventh man.

Jim watched for a moment as Rollin patted the man's shoulder, then he took Barney by the arm and led him away. "All we do is follow that guy and we're at third base."

"Follow him?" asked Barney, puzzled. "There's sure to be guys watching him to see he's not followed – you did say he's the contact next in line to the Big Guy?"

"We follow him electronically, Barney," said Jim. "Rollin stuck a spy-mike on him. We need the rest of our lot for that job."

"Now I get it," laughed Barney.

"We meet the bunch at Macy's. I sure hope Cinnamon has hot coffee lined up; this Christmas is sure a cold one."

Cinnamon and Willy were waiting for them at the lunch-counter in Macy's basement, as arranged.

"All set up, you people," said Jim. "Cinnamon, you and Willy take this." He handed her a small metal case with an aerial about six inches long. "This will tell you when you're on to our man. I'm waiting a call from Rollin as to where he's going."

"Call for a Jim Phelps," said the soda-jerk, casting his eye along the counter.

Jim held up a hand and the clerk handed him the phone. He listened, said "Okay", then replaced the receiver.

"On his way here to Macy's in a cab," he told them. "But that's a blind. He'll pass here and make for Novello Novelties on 42nd Street. Cinnamon and Willy, off you go. We'll be in the crowd as well. I'm aiming to get two birds with one stone. After the exchange, you, Willy, and you, Barney, will take care of the Oringian Santa Claus, while I go after Mr. Big."

It was two o'clock when Santa Claus arrived at the department store on 42nd, and Cinnamon

and Willy were in the crowd awaiting his arrival. Barney was close to them, but they weren't acknowledging each other.

Rollin had said a taxi, but it was a taxi with a difference. It was covered with white cotton-wool, and coloured balloons fluttered from its top. Along the bonnet had been erected card-board cut-outs of two reindeer, and Santa Claus himself sat next to the cabbie. The cops were kept busy holding back the crowd that had gathered.

Willy and Cinnamon fought their way into the mob as Santa was escorted through the press of shoppers, many of whom were children, and they lost sight of Barney.

The box in Cinnamon's hand-bag was pinging loudly, and she put in a hand and turned down the volume.

The toy department was on the fifth floor and, to avoid the crowded elevators, they toiled up the five flights. Willy was

breathless when they arrived in the crowded toy department.

"You're badly out of condi-tion, Willy," said Cinnamon severely.

"Santa Claus!" panted Willy disgustedly. "What'll they think of next?"

The band was playing loudly, and then Santa Claus came out on to the low platform of the display, surrounded by plastic fairies, elves, goblins and comic animal cut-outs. The man sat down on the throne made of plastic icicles and beamed round at the mob of children waiting.

"Come and meet Santa Claus, children," he boomed out. "I've got sacks of fine presents for you all, and when they're empty there's plenty more. Get your tickets and hurry now. There'll be plenty of lucky children this afternoon."

Cinnamon laughed. "Seems almost a pity, Willy," she said reflectively. "All these children really believe that's the real Santa

Claus, the one who comes down their chimneys on Christmas Eve. I wonder what they'd say if we told them that seventeen copies of this one left that employment exchange."

"You wouldn't ever tell them?" said Willy severely.

"What do you take me for?" retorted Cinnamon coldly.

It was after four when their interest was at last alerted. In the queue of children there were quite a few parents, and Cinnamon had her eye on a tall, bulky, well-dressed man with two children in tow, a girl and a boy. He was laughing with the child-ren, but Cinnamon noticed that he was also keeping a wary eye sweeping over the crowds. At the same instant she realised that the listening device in her handbag had ceased to ping. She touched Willy's arm.

"We're being scrambled, Willy," she murmured casually. "See that large man with the girl and boy in red. He's got a neutraliser on him."

"So Barney seems to think," said Willy.

Barney was indeed working his way through the crowd op-posite the part of the queue where the tall man was standing, with the children in red.

The pair from I.M.F. were opposite Santa's throne, but they were pressed tightly into the crowd of fascinated shoppers, all anxiously watching the faces of the children, and especially of their own children.

The tall man stood, benevolent-ly looking down at his girl and boy as Santa began to speak to them. Santa gave them each a present, one for the boy from the sack on his right and one from the left sack for the girl. Laugh-ing, the man shepherded the two children away from the throne, and Willy and Cinnamon began to wriggle through the crowd.

They saw Barney's head above the heads of the crowd opposite, and Willy loosened the gun in his belt. Direct action might be necessary any time.

But the opposition were much too subtle for that.

Barney, watching, saw the man take the parcel from the boy, tear open the paper and put in a hand. Barney was looking across at Willy and Cinnamon, and he nodded his head. Willy plunged forward and, as though by accident, the two parcels were knocked down. The tall stranger gave an angry imprecation.

Willy grabbed one parcel and Cinnamon the other.

But now the crowd, those nearest who had seen the incident, were turning ugly, and the pair faced them desperately. This thing had gone wrong all of a sudden. They would be branded as mean thieves stealing children's presents; they'd be hauled to the manager's office; the police would be called and, true to I.M.F. tradition and regulations, they would be merely two private citizens caught in a most despicable theft.

Barney had managed to get close to the tall man and was knocked against him. There was shouting and whistling.

Barney fell heavily against the man and Cinnamon heard her handbag begin to ping again. But it was fainter now and she grabbed Willy's arm. "Santa's getting away," she hissed.

Willy shoved the two small parcels under his coat and they fought their way through the angry crowd and went behind the curtain at the rear of Santa's icicle throne.

Jim Phelps had been watching from the mezzanine balcony, and now he ran down the stairs and into the toy department just as the tall man was entering the elevator, alone now.

Jim immediately turned and ran down the five flights, only to see his quarry vanishing into a long, sleek car at the kerb. But it could not move away for the press of traffic.

Jim tore his way through the crowd of shoppers and grasped the door-handle of the car. He leaped inside to face his quarry. But all he saw was a closing door on the other side and the man darting out and into the ranks of waiting cars. He went in hot pursuit.

Willy and Cinnamon stood facing two identical figures with white beards and red cloaks and Willy laughed, but his hand was on his pistol. He looked at Cinnamon while the two men stood still, watching them. One of these guys, Willy knew, would be an innocent man working as Santa Claus in the Christmas rush. The other would be their man, the contact who had just handed Mr. Big a package containing the goods they had been ordered to intercept.

"Which one, Cinnamon?" asked Willy, and then Barney came in from one side and a man in morning clothes from the other. The latter spoke first.

"Now then, now then," he said pompously. "There's a great crowd of kids out there, waiting to see Santa Claus. Which of you is on duty?"

"I've done my trick, guvnor," said the Santa on the left, and the other stepped forward.

"My shift now," he grinned through his beard. "You can go now. I'm on until closing time."

"Stop that man," cried Cinnamon, and Barney grabbed the other Santa Claus, who was edging away.

It would have been hard to say whether they had ever seen a man as astonished as that shop manager when he saw Santa Claus whip out a gun from beneath his cloak and start shooting.

But Barney had him in a grapple and had dragged him behind a curtain. Willy and Cinnamon went after them, and the manager began to wring his hands.

Outside, all was pandemonium. The shooting had terrified the crowd and there was a maddened rush for the exits. Police whistles sounded.

It was a wash-room into which the three I.M.F. personnel hustled their captive, and Barney held him in a bear hug, while Willy examined all the fellow's clothing, and found the gun and a flick-knife. Then Barney released him. Like a cornered rat he stood at bay, his white wig awry.

Cinnamon went in quickly. She moved very rapidly and the chop on the side of the neck was like a blur. Barney held up the sagging figure.

"The fire-escape, boys," she said, and opened a window.

Jim Phelps clambered over the bonnets of the cars and trucks that were jammed motionless in 42nd Street, his quarry still in sight. A bullet whistled past his head and the horns of cars sounded. Bedlam was loose in the traffic jam, and Jim was glad of it.

It was on top of a big truck bonnet that Jim finally nailed his prey. The man's long legs were a little late in scrambling up over the hot bonnet, and then the fellow's hands touched the hot metal and he screeched out. Jim had him.

Pulling at both the legs he dragged him down. As he pulled

he gave the stranger a swift clip on the jaw, and when finally he staggered out on to the crowded sidewalk he was supporting an unconscious figure.

"Hey, fella," said a policeman. "What's with your buddy?"

"My father, officer," said Jim solemnly. "Sad case. Keeps getting drunk all the time. Can't do a thing with him, specially at Christmas."

"Say, gee, that's tough," said the sympathetic cop. "Here, down this alley. You'll find a cab rank at the far end. Get the old gent inside. If it hadn't been your old man, I'd have had to take you both in."

"In the other room, Cinnamon, like a good girl, while we strip these characters," said Jim Phelps.

The two parcels of toys had

been examined and nothing had been found that was any use to them. Cinnamon looked curiously over the wreckage of the toys, a small train-set and a plastic kaleidoscope.

"Okay, Jim," she said. "I'll run the rule over these in there. I'll examine them closely for microdots. That's all it can be, unless you find anything on them while I'm out."

The two captives, still unconscious, had been dressed again when she returned, at Jim's signal.

Jim looked dumbly at her, shrugged his shoulders and held out both palms. "Clean as whistles, both," he said. "We've searched every inch of their bodies, teeth, ears, toe-nails, the lot . . . and every stitch of their clothing. Not a thing. No microdots either."

"Take a look at this, Jim," said Cinnamon calmly and she handed him the kaleidoscope. He looked through the eyepiece, shook the tube and rotated it.

"Pretty coloured patterns, that's all I see," he said solemnly.

She put up a hand. "That raised pattern on the tube. See that leaf. Press it and look again."

He pressed the raised leaf and looked. His face changed and he laughed. Isolated letters and figures had begun to appear in among the patterns made by the coloured chips at the bottom of the tube. He took the tube from his eyes and slipped it into his pocket.

"It'll be in code," he said. "But even so, we won't look any more. We made it; we intercepted the message, we got the contact and the big agent. Maybe it is best we know nothing more of what it's all about. And you solved it all single-handed, Cinnamon. Congratulations."

"Oh, I don't know," she said modestly. "I had to use both hands to put it together again."

All Locked Up!

The Mission Impossible team are always being asked to make duplicate keys or pick locks in order to release important prisoners or to get hold of valuable objects or documents vital to the security of the country. The keys vary in shape and size but, like the caveman's rock 'key', they have one thing in common . . . they guard people or valuables from those who wish to steal them.

EARLY LOCKS AND KEYS

The Egyptians were some of the first people to use keys, which fitted into a wooden lock and freed the pins which held the lock secure. The keys themselves were also made from wood, were very cumbersome to use and looked like giant toothbrushes.

The ancient Greeks later invented sickle-shaped keys which fitted through a keyhole, but they were so large that they had to be carried over a man's shoulder.

The Romans had far more ornate keys, made from brass, which they hung as ornaments from a key ring. The locks themselves were made from iron.

In Britain during the Middle Ages one of the most closely guarded keys was the bronze key which would open the inner doors of the castle.

Italian keys of the early seventeenth century were often decorated with beautiful crests of animals and birds on their handles.

UNUSUAL TREASURES

In the Middle Ages gold and jewels were hidden away in strong chests, each with two locks, one visible in which a key would not fit, the real lock hidden in a secret compartment in the lid. Other things were also kept under lock and key, things which today lie openly on the kitchen shelves.

These included many different spices, which were very expensive to buy in those times and were kept in jewelled caskets, to which only the mistress of the household had the key. This hung securely from a chain fastened to her belt so that servants would not use them too liberally in cooking, or even steal them to sell at a profit.

The Victorian housewife, in later years, carried a similar key to the store cupboard and doled out all ingredients for cooking and even the food itself very sparingly, especially the amount eaten by the servants.

Other treasures always carefully locked away were the rich vestments, beautifully embroidered with glowing silks and sometimes encrusted with jewels, which were worn by high-ranking churchmen. When these were not worn they were stored away in special chests which can still be seen in some churches today.